BEETHOVEN: MASTER MUSICIAN

Books by Madeleine Goss

BEETHOVEN: MASTER MUSICIAN

DEEP-FLOWING BROOK: The Story of Johann Sebastian Bach

BOLERO: The Life of Maurice Ravel

UNFINISHED SYMPHONY: The Story of Franz Schubert

BRAHMS: THE MASTER

(with Robert Haven Schauffler)

BEETHOVEN

MASTER MUSICIAN

by MADELEINE GOSS

Beethoven's Birthplace

Illustrations by Carl Schultheiss

NEW YORK: HENRY HOLT AND COMPANY

To the Memory of My Grandfather

C. W. LEFFINGWELL, D.D., LL.D.

CONTENTS

CONTENTS

BEETHOVEN MUSIC EXAMPLES

BEETHOVEN: MASTER MUSICIAN

CHAPTER I

THE ATTIC IN BONN

(1 7 7 0 - 7 3)

A SOLITARY CANDLE stood by the bed in the poor, low-ceilinged room. Its dim flame threw wavering shadows against the cracked walls and shabby furniture; but over the woman and her newborn child it cast a soft halo of light.

Maria-Magdalena raised herself on one elbow and listened sadly to the steps going down the stairs. "Jan!" she called pleadingly. "Don't leave me . . ."

The loud slamming of the front door was her only

I

answer. In startled terror, the baby awoke and cried out sharply.

"Hush, little heart," she said, holding him close. "Don't be frightened. Nothing can harm you." But the harsh noise still echoed in the child's ears and he refused to be comforted. Finally his mother crooned to him—old German lullabies and half-forgotten folk songs from her girlhood days—while outside, the wind wailed a soft accompaniment. Gradually the little one stopped crying.

For very loneliness Maria-Magdalena began to talk to him.

"Why must your father spend all his time in that dreadful place?" Her voice broke, and she held the baby closer. "I thought tonight that he would surely stay with us!" She had prayed so earnestly that the coming of their child would keep Jan away from the tavern and the evil companions there. He was not a bad man, Jan van Beethoven, but a weakling who couldn't resist his passion for drink. Maria-Magdalena shuddered as she remembered the nights —alas, all too frequent—when he had been drinking too heavily, and came back to their attic home shouting coarse songs and oaths.

Tonight she had been sure that he would not leave her. He had seemed so proud of his newborn son. "He's no beauty," Jan admitted, shaking his head regretfully, "but maybe he'll be like the ugly duckling—and some day turn into a swan!" He rolled his eyes expressively. "*Such* a swan he'll be! Just wait and see, Maria," and he had laughed, his great loud laugh that filled the tiny garret.

Maria had joined in timidly, a bit resentful at his criticism of her precious baby, but not daring to show it. Who was she to remonstrate with Jan van Beethoven? Was he not, in spite of his poverty, a musician of standing, and descended from a fine family? While she was only the daughter of a cook! She was never allowed to forget that Jan had been out of his mind when he married her. But perhaps now they would forgive her—if only this little one survived.

December 16, 1770. Almost a Christmas child! Maria-Magdalena heard the carillon of bells on the tower of the electoral palace practicing the carols for the following week. "I must write the date in the big Bible," she thought. "Some day when he is a great man perhaps he will look back on the writing and think of his poor mother." She smiled wistfully. "Some day when he is a great musician —like his grandfather, only greater. Like his father, only much, much greater!"

There was a sound below and a step on the stairs. Maria-Magdalena's heart gave a leap. Had Jan come back after all?

But it was only the baby's grandfather.

The door opened softly, and a large head crowned with

3

shaggy gray hair peered through the crack. Ludwig van Beethoven was a powerful old man, rather short and thick-set, but still strong in spite of his bent back. His black eyes flashed fire when he was angry, and it was easy to see where Jan's violent temper came from. But the resemblance ended there, for old Ludwig was the soul of honor, and it was the sorrow of his life that his son should be so dissipated.

The old man tiptoed clumsily across the narrow room, holding in his hands a bowl covered with a coarse blue handkerchief. He could hardly stand upright in the low attic, and he was so intent on keeping his soup from spilling that he did not look up until he reached the bedside.

"Where is Jan?" he asked sharply when he saw that Maria-Magdalena was alone.

She tried to make excuses for her husband. "We were sleeping, the little one and I." She looked up at her father-in-law timidly. "Jan was so tired of sitting here. He has just gone for a little walk."

Old Ludwig scowled and kicked savagely at a chair. "Bah! I know those little walks and where they lead to!"

The baby, frightened by his grandfather's rough voice, began to cry.

"See!" said Maria-Magdalena. "He cannot stand harsh sounds!" She watched the old man shyly. "Jan says that he is born with a musician's ear."

The old man roared with laughter. Surprised at the new sound, the child suddenly stopped his wailing and looked up at his grandfather. There seemed to be an instinctive attraction between the two, and when old Ludwig reached down his arms, the baby suffered himself to be taken up without protest.

The grandfather examined him critically and shook his head in doubt.

"Are they always as ugly as this?" He looked at his daughter-in-law as if she were to blame. But in reality the baby, with his thick shock of black hair and small deep-set eyes, was much more like his grandfather than his mother. Maria-Magdalena was devoted to her family and deeply sensitive to everything that was beautiful, but her personality was as colorless as her appearance. Old Ludwig's pride had been cut to the quick when his son had married so far beneath him. But he had gradually come to feel a certain pity and affection for the gentle ways of his faithful daughter-in-law.

As he looked down at the baby in his arms, the old man hoped that this child would make up to him for all that he had suffered through his own son. He would see to it that the boy traveled straight! A great affection for the little being came over the man. "What will you name him?" he asked tenderly.

Maria-Magdalena hung her head as if she were not sure

that he would approve. "It seemed—" she murmured—
"we thought it should be Ludwig."

"Ludwig!" he exclaimed. "But that was the name of
the child you lost last year."

"Yes, Father—Ludwig-Maria. But he lived such a very
short time!" Her eyes filled with tears. "And since this
little one has come to take his place. . . . Besides, it is
your name!"

The old man shook his head doubtfully. "Bad luck,
child—bad luck. . . ."

Little Ludwig stiffened himself in his grandfather's arms
and began to complain softly, as if the words were a
prophecy which he somehow knew would be fulfilled.

The little one seemed always to be listening. Sometimes
there was a rapt expression on his face, but sometimes there
was a scowl, and then Maria-Magdalena came to expect
the storm that was sure to follow. A strong-willed child
he was—strong in his affections and violent when he was
crossed. His mother had known him to fly into a tantrum
of temper because someone had unwittingly slammed a
door.

The old grandfather would shake his head when the

child stiffened himself in rage and began to turn black with the violence of his emotions.

"Maria, we must not allow it—he will end like his poor grandmother!" and, remembering the sad fate of his own wife, whose passion for drink had forced him to put her under restraint in a convent, the old man would sternly shake the child and tell him to be still.

On the other hand, how beautiful the smile on little Ludwig's face when he was listening to something that pleased him! Maria-Magdalena would try to hear what it was, but she, poor soul, was insensible to the melodies that bewitched him. The sighing of the wind through the trees, faint church bells in the distance (the air in Bonn seemed always full of church bells), the humming of insects, or the river Rhine singing its way down the valley—these and a thousand other sounds that most people never even noticed were music in his ears.

The river fascinated him especially. He loved to watch its quiet, unhurried progress and listen to the soft murmur of the water. In the distance he could see the gentle peaks of the Seven Sisters—seven watchful guardians, they seemed to Ludwig—protecting the placid Rhine valley from all harm.

Soon little Ludwig wanted to explore for himself the fascinating outer world. The stairs from his attic home were very steep. But he managed to climb laboriously down and find his way into the little walled garden beneath.

Then one day, when the outer gate had been left ajar, he slipped through and wandered down the narrow street to the fields beyond. After that it was impossible to keep him at home. As soon as his mother's back was turned he would be out and into the fields. There he would lie down in the midst of the flowers, absorbed in watching the insects, playing with bits of grass and sticks—completely wrapped up in a world of his own.

Maria-Magdalena soon learned that he was safer left to his own devices than when she tried to keep him close to her. After a few attempts at discipline, when she brought him back by main force and he screamed with rage for the rest of the day, she resigned herself to his strange passion for the outdoors and let him go when he pleased.

One warm summer's day, as he lay on his back in the fields watching the clouds go by and listening to the songs of the birds, he heard, far in the distance, a faint music of singular sweetness. It was only a herd of cows moving homeward, the tinkling of their bells mingled with the plaintive song of the herdsman, but it thrilled the child strangely. He listened with deep intensity, straining to

8

catch the sound until his whole being was lifted up and carried into a new world—a world filled with light and vibrant harmony.

Ludwig never knew how long that breathless moment lasted. Time ceased to exist, and when he finally came to himself he felt strange and bewildered, as if he had come back to a foreign land.

All through his life the beauty of that moment remained with him. As he grew older it ripened into a deep conviction that the source of true music must be found in Nature. He was forever seeking to recapture the ecstasy he had experienced that day. And when, after hours of still and patient waiting, a little of its joy returned, he would be filled with happiness and a desire to share his inspiration with others.

Old Ludwig was determined that his grandson should not follow in his father's footsteps.

"But, Maria, what if he *is* only two and a half years old? His religious education must not be neglected."

Maria-Magdalena smiled and shrugged her shoulders. It was better to humor the whims of the old grandfather than to oppose him. He seemed to have a vague hope that through his own prayers and piety he could make up for the growing dissipation of his son Jan. The sooner little Ludwig was taken to church, the better.

"How about it, little mouse, would you like to go to the chapel with Grosspapa?"

Ludwig's eyes brightened. *Anywhere* with Grosspapa he was content. The two trudged off together towards the court chapel.

What a magnificent place it was! Little Ludwig was awed by the stately pillars and stained-glass windows. He longed to walk around and examine these new curiosities, but his grandfather sternly motioned him to sit still.

"But, Grosspapa, *why?*"

"Hush!" came the warning whisper.

This was no fun! Usually, when he and Grandfather went out together, they had a glorious lark. There were stories and shouts of laughter, and sometimes a bag of peppermint drops. He wished he hadn't come. . . . Tears began to gather in his eyes.

Then suddenly a miracle happened. With a rush of sound the organ pealed forth, and the church was filled with music.

Ludwig sat transfixed, enthralled with the sound. His tears forgot to fall, and it was no longer necessary to remind him to be silent. He was so rapt that nothing existed for him but the music.

Old Ludwig watched him out of the corner of his eye, well content with the effect he had produced. He didn't know at that moment which he hoped the more—that the child's absorbed attention betokened unusual musical interest or that it meant a sudden awakening of religious fervor. He wished, of course, that the boy would be musical (were not all the Beethovens musicians?), but at the same time he half hoped that he might want to enter the Church.

Gradually the organ became softer, and a rich tenor sang out to its accompaniment. The old man nudged his young companion and looked to see if he would recognize the singer. It was Jan, the boy's father, tenor of the court chapel. At first the child didn't know the voice which at home he had been accustomed to hear raised in ribald songs. He was too young to understand that it was only on old Ludwig's account that Jan retained his position. Old Ludwig was the director of the court orchestra, an honored post that he had held since shortly after his arrival in Bonn from Flanders, forty years before, and out of regard for him, the Elector allowed the old man's worthless son to sing in the church.

Jan, when he was sober, had an unusually fine voice, and to the child, who had never really heard him sing before, he seemed suddenly to have become a changed being, strangely glorified and exalted.

Ever after, when his father was beside himself with drink, little Ludwig would watch him closely, trying vainly to find some traces of the angel whose voice he had heard that day in the church.

Ludwig and his grandfather became inseparable companions. The child was unusually intelligent for his age, and the old man took him with him everywhere. They went together on long rambles through the country. Occasionally they took an excursion down the river—their beloved "Father Rhine." And then what a joy it was to the child to be carried on the very bosom of that mighty stream which he had watched by the hour from its banks! He would choose a seat close to the bow of the boat, his hand tight held within his grandfather's, and listen to the soft swish of the water against the sides.

One day, however, the grandfather did not appear for their accustomed walk. Ludwig waited for him, impatient to be off. There was a bird's nest in the woods near by, full of little blue eggs just ready to hatch. He decided he would go on without him.

But the eggs were not yet hatched, and somehow the woods were much less interesting than usual. He missed the cheerful voice and hearty laugh of his grandfather. Finally he went back to get him.

Old Ludwig's little house stood on the very edge of the town, surrounded by a tiny garden in which he loved to work. The child looked anxiously about for his grandfather, but the familiar figure was not in its accustomed place, stooping over the pansy bed or weeding the cabbage patch.

Ludwig felt a vague apprehension as he neared the house and saw all the blinds closely drawn. He heard strange voices and the sound of weeping.

"*Na, na,* Maria—it is better thus! To go so quickly . . ."

Ludwig pushed open the door with a trembling hand.

Inside, the closed shutters filled the room with gloom. He could hardly make out what was going on, but at last he discovered his mother weeping bitterly and surrounded by neighbors who were trying to comfort her. His father sat on a chair in the corner with his face in his hands, groaning loudly.

"*Mütterchen,* what is it?" he cried, in an agony of fear.

At sight of him, his mother's tears redoubled, and she caught him closely to her. "*Ach,* little heart . . . how can I tell you!"

His grandfather had died suddenly from a stroke of apoplexy.

For a long time Ludwig could not realize what had

happened. Each morning he awoke with the certainty that today, at last, his grandfather would come back to him. Each night he crept into bed a little lonelier, a little more perplexed. He roamed the fields in search of his companion.

Even the great outdoors with its beloved sounds failed to comfort him.

CHAPTER II

THE WONDER BOX

(1 7 7 4)

AFTER THE LOSS of his grandfather, little Ludwig became more quiet and reserved than ever. The old man had been his one companion, and, perhaps because of the strong similarity between the two, he was the only person who really understood the child's shy yet forceful nature. No one could fill the grandfather's place in the little one's heart.

15

Only one thing remained to Ludwig of his beloved comrade, and if he had not begged to be allowed to keep it, even that would have been sold with the rest of the old man's belongings to pay Jan's debts. It was a portrait in oil of old Ludwig van Beethoven painted by the court artist Radoux at the time of the grandfather's greatest glory as chapel master of the Elector's orchestra. It showed the old man standing proudly erect, a tasseled cap on his head and a roll of music, the emblem of his profession, in his hand.

Ludwig did not care much for other children. He had been too constantly the companion of his grandfather to feel at home with the youngsters of the neighborhood. To Ludwig's quiet, thoughtful disposition, their games and play seemed foolish and pointless. He would gradually draw to one side and watch them, much as older people watch the antics of young animals at play. Occasionally their pranks would strike him as tremendously funny, and he would roar with laughter. The other children, unable to understand the reason for his gaiety, resented his attitude, and Ludwig was never a welcome playfellow.

But he didn't mind. He would far rather wander alone in the fields and listen to his beautiful sounds than play the most amusing games with other children.

Only his mother seemed to understand the sensitive child. "Little heart, where are you going? To play with the other children?" It was a sort of game with them.

"Well, perhaps," he would answer; but they both knew that he was headed for the meadows, away from the senseless chatter of those others, and close to the voice of the great outdoors whose language he understood.

The rainy days were the worst. Then, try as he would, he could not get by his watchful mother. After several successful flights, when he had returned hours later, dripping wet and, more often than not, with a bad cold, Maria-Magdalena proved adamant about excursions in the rain.

She would shake her head regretfully when he begged to go out.

"*Nein, nein,* little one. Not today!" and quickly, dreading the scene which usually followed: "Besides, I am so lonely. You would not leave me?"

This was the one way to avert trouble. Ludwig's ungovernable temper when once aroused was almost impossible to control. But he loved his mother dearly, and for her sake he was willing to make the most tremendous sacrifices.

So with a sigh he would climb to his favorite spot by the tiny dormer window and sit watching the gray skies and the little garden below. He could hear the sound of the raindrops pattering on the roof or tinkling against the window panes in a sudden gust of wind. Their gentle music fascinated him. For hours he would sit, listening intently, humming over to himself the song of the wind-blown showers.

It was on just such a rainy day that the great adventure happened. Years later, Ludwig looked back on that gray morning with mingled joy and sorrow. For it was the beginning of his life's work, and also the cause of untold drudgery and misery in his childish existence.

On this particular day Ludwig had been sitting so long in his accustomed spot by the window that he had grown tired of it. He turned hopefully to his mother for entertainment, only to find that she had slipped out—probably on an errand to the baker's, or perhaps to fetch water from the well in the courtyard below.

He wandered around disconsolately and began his usual exploration of the narrow attic which served them as a home. There were only two small rooms, so close under the eaves that a tall man could touch the ceiling with his head. First the tiny chamber, dimly lit by one narrow window, where Ludwig had been born. Then the other room, which was more like a hall, with the staircase coming right up into it. This second room had to serve as both kitchen and general living quarters, and it was hardly large enough to hold the few possessions that belonged to the little family.

Everything there was familiar to Ludwig. He knew each nook and corner by heart; each piece of furniture and shabby object had its own special meaning and significance for him.

Each? Suddenly his heart leaped. He peered down the stairway to see whether there were any signs of his mother's return. All was still.

With his heart strangely beating, the child drew closer to the corner where stood a large box whose mystery had fascinated him for some time. It was the one unknown object among others too well known. Ludwig could not remember the day when it was brought—a whim of his father's, who had promptly forgotten about it as soon as he had given strict orders that it must never be touched. Maria-Magdalena grumbled over the amount of space it took up in their crowded quarters, but she stood in too great fear of her husband to remonstrate openly.

On the rare occasions when Ludwig was tempted to disobey his father's command, his mother reproved him in an unusually stern voice.

"You are never, *never* to touch that. Do you understand?"

He had obeyed her dutifully, but each time the attraction of this unknown thing had grown upon him. One day, as his mother was cleaning and had carefully moved the box away from the wall, he heard a strange sound come from within. What could it have been? The child stood spellbound until his mother laughingly moved him to make way for her cleaning.

Today the desire to investigate the forbidden box was so strong that it became an irresistible impulse. He drew nearer slowly and looked carefully to see how it might be opened. At last he found the lid, a curious hinged affair that opened in the center of the box and exposed to his surprised view a long row of shiny, flat sticks, with other narrower black ones in between.

In spite of his serious ways and unusual intelligence, little Ludwig was not much more than a baby at this time, scarcely past his fourth birthday. And, like all babies, his first impulse was to touch, to learn through his fingers what this queer thing might be.

Gently one little finger reached out and touched a white key. A tinkle like a fairy flute came from within the magic box.

Ludwig's astonishment was so great that he drew his finger away; immediately the sound ceased. He tried another key—another, higher flute answered.

The child was enraptured. He wanted to explore each separate key of the wonderful instrument. But at that moment he heard his mother at the door, and in a panic over what he had done, he closed the lid and ran to his seat by the window.

"So now, little mouse, you are still listening to the rain? I'll wager you didn't even know that I had gone to the baker's for a loaf of bread!" She put her hand caressingly on his head. Something in the entranced expression on his face struck her, and she looked at him more closely.

"What is it, child? Have you seen a vision?"

Little Ludwig longed to throw his arms around her neck and tell her of his wonderful discovery, but he feared too much her anger at his disobedience.

After that eventful day, Ludwig was always watching for a chance to be alone with the magic box. It was even more wonderful to him than the music of the fields, the birds, and the rain, for he could find all those sounds within the strange instrument. Even the roll of the thunder was there, down toward the end of the shiny keys. There was the hammering of the blacksmith, too, and the noise of the big bass drum which old Hans pounded out with such solemnity on holidays in the market place.

By running his fingers softly and quickly up and down the keys, Ludwig could make the sound of the wind in the trees, and soon he found the calls of the birds and the chirp of the cricket. It was an unending source of delight to him, and whenever he had a chance to be alone with the box, he would draw near with beating heart to see what new secrets he could learn.

He tried experiments, first with one hand, then with the other. He found that he could make a tune that sounded like the village band. Up above was the horn—Ludwig could not help laughing when he thought of Peter, blowing until he was red in the face—then down below was old Hans, banging away on his drum. One chubby hand was old Hans, marking time rhythmically; the other was Peter, blowing and blowing. . . .

Suddenly he felt a hand on his shoulder.

He jumped around in terror and saw his father standing behind him.

Ludwig was panic-stricken to find that he had been discovered touching the forbidden object. Jan's word was law, and the child stood in such fear of his father's wrath that he trembled now and turned pale. But to his astonishment nothing happened. Instead of the expected blow his father spoke to him in a gentle voice.

"What are you doing, Ludwig?"

The child hung his head and was afraid to answer.

"What were you playing there?"

Emboldened by the unusual lenience in his voice, Ludwig looked up shyly. A sudden flow of love for this new kind father filled his heart. Perhaps he could make him understand about the wonders of the box. Timidly he tried to explain the fascination of the keys—how they had tempted him to disobey.

Jan listened carefully, with evident interest. Ludwig was overjoyed; perhaps his father understood the secrets of the magic instrument and could show him more about it?

With a smile Jan pulled up a chair and sat down before the old clavier. He let his fingers wander idly over the keys for a moment; then all at once a rush of music filled the little room. The child clasped his hands tightly together and stood entranced, scarcely breathing.

Jan had inherited a good measure of his father's ability. If he had been willing to work hard enough he might have become a musician of note. In his younger days old Ludwig had kept him sternly at his practice, but in later years Jan's indolent nature and loose ways had made him more and more neglectful of his work.

When he had bought the old clavier some time before— a poor broken-down thing at best, but picked up at a bargain—Jan thought he would practice daily and regain some of his earlier skill. But he never got around to it. Either he was too tired, or else some of his worthless companions would drag him off just when he was beginning to feel in the mood to play. As a consequence, when he sat down to play for the boy, his performance was far from perfect. But to Ludwig, with his passion for beautiful sounds, the music was a revelation.

When Jan had finished playing he turned to his son. The boy's eyes were glowing with enthusiasm, and his father—easily flattered—was highly gratified at the impression he had made.

"So . . . little one, it pleases you?" He put his arm around the delighted child and stroked his hair with condescending gentleness. "Would you like to learn to play like that?"

Ludwig drew in his breath sharply. He could hardly believe that this was his own father speaking to him. How good—how noble he was!

But at that moment a thought had struck the father, and there was a reason behind his sudden kindness—a reason far less unselfish and noble than his son believed.

Jan van Beethoven had heard much about a child prodigy named Wolfgang Amadeus Mozart. By the time Ludwig was born, Mozart, a boy of fourteen, had become one of the leading musicians of Europe, and on the day that Jan found his son playing the forbidden clavier, Mozart was the idol of all the musical world.

Jan had recently found a new crony who had come to Bonn with a theatrical troupe and had much to tell about the childhood of Mozart. This new companion, Tobias Pfeiffer, was a disreputable sort of fellow, too fond of drinking and carousing; but Jan learned that Pfeiffer had formerly been a prominent musician in Frankfurt.

He never tired of telling about the time when he, Tobias Pfeiffer, had been invited (here he would clear his throat and swell visibly with pride) to suggest a theme for Mozart to improvise upon. Jan thought it hardly possible that a character like Pfeiffer had ever stood high enough to be on such friendly terms with the great musician, but at the same time he never tired of hearing about the wonderful success of the youthful Mozart, and more especially the great sums of money which the boy earned while still a very small child.

Jan's mind fastened itself greedily on the thought. Music —child—money! Here was an easy way to grow rich; if only his little Ludwig had inherited the family talent for music, he might be made into a second Mozart. Plenty of money, then, for all the drinks Jan wanted. . . . Perhaps the boy might even earn enough to make the family comfortable. Jan van Beethoven was no tight-fisted miser. He was willing to share with the family if there should be more than enough for his own needs.

So when he discovered young Ludwig at the clavier, he was highly pleased. He turned graciously toward his son. Could he not be trained even as Father Mozart had trained the young Wolfgang?

Jan was enough of a musician to see that four-year-old

Ludwig had unusual talent. With a little time and effort he was sure that he could teach him to play well. And then they would travel all over the country. . . . Jan could see himself leading in his son clad in a suit of violet-colored satin—he could fairly hear the applause of multitudes acclaiming his own son as the new child prodigy. It was a wonderful idea!

He stood little Ludwig on a stool in front of the clavier, and with the greatest patience and kindliness gave him his first lesson.

The boy was thrilled. He watched with absorbed interest every move his father made, and soon mastered the little exercises he showed him. Jan was delighted with the eager response of the child, and became so interested in teaching him that he lost all count of time and place.

Several hours later Maria-Magdalena returned to find them still at work.

"Jan—Ludwig! What are you doing?" she exclaimed with surprise as she saw the two before the ancient instrument.

Ludwig ran to her ecstatically.

"Mother, Mother darling . . . dear Father is teaching me to make music on the wonder box!" Nothing would do but she must hear each note that he had learned.

Again after supper, Jan, afraid that the child might forget what he had learned, made him go over his lesson once more. At first the little one was all enthusiasm, but soon, worn out by the intense effort of the day, his fingers began to drag.

Then the father grew impatient and spoke to him sharply. "Do you suppose you can learn to play without *practice?*" he asked sarcastically.

Little Ludwig applied himself wearily once more, and went patiently over his lesson again.

CHAPTER III

A NEW MASTER

(1776)

JAN NOW BECAME OBSESSED by the determination to make Ludwig into another child prodigy. For once the man's indolent nature was spurred to activity by his hopes for the future. He devoted long hours every day to teaching the child; even his old cronies at the tavern saw him seldom.

Maria-Magdalena was delighted at the change in her

husband, yet she kept an anxious eye on Ludwig in fear lest the strain would be too much for him.

And it was not long before the reaction came.

Ludwig soon found that the joy he had first experienced in sounding the notes and trying to make music was lost in the maze of scales and five-finger exercises which his father made him practice. To him there was no sense in the interminable notes he was forced to play. He felt that he had been cheated by his father, who had promised to teach him to make *music*.

"But, Father, this is not what you told me I should learn!" he would cry, tears in his eyes.

"Hush, little stupid!" was the cross reply. "Don't you know that you can never learn anything without hard work first?"

Then Ludwig would begin again on the tiresome exercises, hoping that soon he might be able to play real music. He did learn, with incredible speed. Jan was amazed at the boy's ability, but he grew more exacting as the child progressed. He forced him to practice many hours each day, and often in the evening when friends came in, he would make Ludwig show off all that he had taught him.

Soon the boy began to lose interest and to dread the hours of work instead of looking forward to them as he had done at first. Then he openly rebelled.

When his father found that the desire to learn beautiful

sounds was no longer sufficient to keep him at his practice, he tried different tactics. If Ludwig stopped for a moment to rest or watch the clouds through the window, the stern face of his father would peer over his shoulder.

"Ludwig, what are you dreaming of now? If you don't work harder, there will be no supper for you tonight." Usually this threat was sufficiently dreadful, for Ludwig was a strong, hearty boy, and he loved his food.

But the hours of work grew so tiresome that he decided he would rather go without eating than do the hated practicing.

Then his father grew very stern. The next time the boy refused to practice, Jan drew out a long strap. . . .

Ludwig, however, was as strong-willed as his father, and from his grandfather he had inherited a stubbornness that was equaled only by his love of justice. He felt in his childish heart that his father had no right to make him work so cruelly, when most boys of his age were playing out of doors. What few hours he had to himself were embittered by thoughts of the drudgery to come, and he could not even lie in the fields as he had been accustomed to do and listen to the melody of wind and birds. All he could hear now was the noise of the scales or silly exercises drumming up and down the keyboard.

A battle of wills began between the father and his small son. Jan was determined that Ludwig should work as he directed. The child was equally determined that he would not. He would grit his teeth when the blows of the strap descended and try not to cry out; but finally, from very exhaustion he would have to give in. Each time it was the same story.

Jan took care, when a lesson was due, to send Maria-Magdalena away on an errand. He well knew what a scene she would make if she saw the methods he was using to force Ludwig to his will. Maria-Magdalena stood in fear and trembling of her husband, but her love for her child was stronger than her fear. She would protect him at any cost.

But Jan himself was desperate. His meager salary was barely sufficient to keep the family from starving. And that little he was all too ready to squander at the tavern. Ludwig was his one hope.

Maria-Magdalena began to suspect that something was wrong. The boy looked pale and sad. His appetite was no longer good; he moped and hid himself in a corner.

The next time her husband sent her to the store on an errand, Maria-Magdalena left dutifully, but she returned a few moments later.

The struggle between Ludwig and his father had already started when she got back. She stood at the door for a moment, speechless with indignation. Then she ran to Ludwig and caught him closely to her.

"Jan—Jan!" she cried fiercely. "You *must* not—you *shall* not!"

The man turned on her in a fury, with strap uplifted. The blows rained on her shoulders, but she hardly felt them in her concern for her child.

To Ludwig, however, it was a terrible thing to see his mother struck. He could not bear it for a moment, and in an agony of self-reproach he threw himself on his knees before his father and burst into a passion of tears.

"Father—stop! I'll do anything you say. . . ."

With a grim smile the man lowered his hand. "You shouldn't interfere, good wife," he said. "It is only through Ludwig that we shall be able to keep from starving. . . ."

The boy listened intently as Jan told Maria-Magdalena how desperate their circumstances were, how greatly Ludwig was to help them.

After that it was no longer necessary to beat the child to make him work. He was more than eager to progress, to earn money so that his mother might have white bread and a silk dress.

"See, Ludwig—here is a new way to make your precious music!" Jan held up a decrepit old violin that had been given him by one of his friends at the tavern who was too far gone to care about it any longer.

The boy looked at the instrument with shining eyes, and when his father tucked it under his chin and played a brief melody, Ludwig could hardly wait to try it himself.

Jan watched him with crafty eyes. He had been disappointed in his son's career as a child prodigy. In the first place, it took money to go on a concert tour, and they had none. Then Jan had no influence, no prominent friends or wealthy patron. So Ludwig's remarkable talent was known only to a few, and the family continued to be destitute. Perhaps the violin would be a way out of their difficulties. There was always a demand for good violinists in the orchestra.

At first Ludwig was enchanted with the sweet tones of the new instrument. But when he found that it was only an excuse to add more hours to his already burdensome practice, his joy disappeared, and the violin became a grim reality.

The Beethoven family had recently moved from the Bonngasse, where Ludwig was born, to another house on the Rheingasse. From the window Ludwig could see the river Rhine, winding into the distance toward the mountains called the Seven Sisters. One day as he was playing on his violin he made a discovery. He had been practicing diligently for some time, only half conscious of the work his fingers were doing while he watched the river dreamily through the window. Suddenly he noticed that he was playing something far different from the stupid exercises his father made him learn.

The rhythm had a vaguely familiar sound, with its soothing, flowing tones. Ludwig listened as if someone else were playing. Then he recognized what it was—the melody that always ran through his head when he watched the stately flowing Rhine. He was surprised and delighted. Over and over he played the lovely air, his song of the river—his very own. The ugly exercises were forgotten.

The harsh voice of his father broke in on his enchantment.

"What silly trash are you scratching together now, Ludwig?" He snatched the violin from the boy. "You know I can't bear that! Do your exercises and leave this scratching alone."

Ludwig learned so rapidly that in a few years he knew all that his father had to teach him. He began to get an occasional engagement to play at rich homes, and while his small earnings were nothing in comparison with what

Jan had dreamed of, still, they helped to give the family a few comforts.

As he grew older, the boy found his greatest delight in fashioning little melodies of his own, though he took good care not to let his father hear him. But one day Ludwig discovered a tune that pleased him so much that he thought he would play it for his father and let him think it was something he had learned.

Jan, however, was not to be taken in. He looked sternly at the boy.

"That is something you have made up. Won't you ever stop, after all I have told you? Play your exercises and pieces correctly; that is more important. Later you can make up things of your own, but not now. You are not ready yet!"

"Father . . . !" Ludwig interrupted in anguished tones.

Jan turned in surprise to find the boy staring at an empty spot on the wall.

"Now what's the trouble?" he asked carelessly.

"Grandfather's portrait—where is it gone?" The child could hardly speak.

"The portrait? Perhaps your mother—" he began craftily, but he stopped as he saw the dangerous look in Ludwig's eyes.

"Well, if you must know, I sold it at the pawnshop," he exclaimed defiantly, and, as he noted the fury in the child's face he added quickly, "to buy new clothes for your mother."

Ludwig's shoulders shook with dry, hard sobs. Life was too cruel; the things he cared for were always taken from him! He seized his father's arm.

"Please, Father, please! I will work and earn the money in some way if *only* you will buy Grandfather's portrait back again."

Jan was already ashamed of his action in selling the last thing left to him of his father. "Perhaps, child," he agreed with ill grace.

Ludwig found the shop where Jan had taken the picture. A bent old man with black skullcap and horn-rimmed spectacles was the proprietor, and Ludwig begged to be allowed to work for him until he should have earned enough to buy back the beloved portrait. Fortunately for Ludwig, the old proprietor was a soft-hearted man. For many weeks thereafter the boy spent all his spare time working so that he might regain the precious likeness of his grandfather. The portrait became to him a symbol of all the joy and companionship which he lacked so pitifully, and until he died it remained his most treasured possession.

Ludwig was asleep on his narrow cot in an alcove just off the attic. When night came he was usually so exhausted that he fell into bed half-dressed. It was a heavy burden for a nine-year-old boy to spend so many hours each day practicing and to feel himself responsible for the main part of his family's support.

Often he would be awakened in the middle of the night by the noisy return of his father from the tavern, singing and shouting and rousing the entire household.

Tonight, Jan had brought a friend with him, and they had both been drinking heavily.

"See, Maria, who is with me!" he called loudly. "Ah, you don't know what luck we have tonight!"

Maria-Magdalena, who had been dozing in her chair while she waited for her husband to return, looked up half-asleep.

Jan put his arm affectionately around his companion's neck. *"Ach,* Tobias, thou art a true friend!" He was almost inclined to weep over the goodness of his friend.

"Think, Maria," Jan continued sentimentally, "Tobias has agreed to come here and share our humble quarters!"

Maria looked bewildered. She could see no great nobility in that.

"But what is more," Jan clapped his friend waggishly on the shoulder, "he has promised to give the boy lessons." He lowered his voice and looked toward the alcove. Ludwig, behind his curtain, was all ears.

"You do not know what a great musician Tobias is!" Jan went on. "He was once chief oboist in the Frankfurt orchestra; and more—" he spoke with reverence in his voice—"he is a *composer!*"

Tobias Pfeiffer had fallen into bad ways. As the years went by, he had given way more and more to his passion for drink and had gradually sunk to an insignificant position with a theatrical troupe. Now he was very glad to find a place to eat and sleep in return for giving a few lessons.

Ludwig, listening eagerly from his bed, heard only the great fact that his new master was a composer. Perhaps Tobias would teach him to "scratch his own tunes," as his father called it. He could hardly wait until morning to begin.

Fortunately, he was not disappointed. Pfeiffer recognized the boy's genius and saw that with the proper instruction Ludwig might become a great composer. To be sure, there were many rules to learn, for in those days everything had to be done according to a set pattern. But to Ludwig it was like having the outline of a beautiful picture that he could fill in with as many lovely colors as he liked.

What matter that Tobias was even more erratic in his

hours than his father had been? Ludwig never minded, and when the two men came singing from the tavern late at night and woke him up he was always ready to work.

"Come, now, Ludwig," Tobias would cry, seizing the child good-naturedly by the arm and dragging him from his bed. "Let us have a little music. . . ."

Half-asleep and rubbing his eyes, Ludwig would stumble to the clavier. The candle always threw long shadows in the corners. . . . The clock in the market-place tower would begin to strike loudly—ten . . . eleven . . . twelve . . .

Pfeiffer would shake him roughly. "Wake up and get to work!"

When he was once thoroughly aroused and into the music, young Beethoven no longer wished to sleep. Sometimes it was daybreak before they stopped, and when he crept back into his cold bed, lights danced before his tired eyes, and his head ached violently. The windows were all kept well closed for fear of the night air, and in his little alcove the atmosphere was stifling.

The strenuous days and restless nights, together with an almost total lack of exercise, began to weaken Ludwig's naturally strong constitution. He was too tired to go outdoors when his work was finished. The pains in his head prevented him from sleeping; his heart took spells of beating violently, and he would break out into cold perspiration.

He began to fear that he was going to die. How terrible it would be if, after all this work, just when he would soon be ten years old and ready to earn enough to make the family comfortable, he should come to an untimely end!

A deep sadness came over him. With his sensitive nature he suffered both physically and mentally and came to believe that everyone was against him. It was as if a cruel fate had set him apart from his fellow men, and ordained that he must be friendless.

The feeling remained with him until his death.

Two younger brothers had come to the family since Ludwig's birth. Carl, the elder—red-headed and ugly— was like his father, lazy and irresponsible. Johann was more serious in temperament, but selfish and hard-hearted.

They cared nothing for Ludwig, but in spite of their indifference he was devoted to them. When, as the eldest, he was left to look after the younger ones, he would show remarkable patience in his care of them. Yet they took advantage of his affection at every turn and seemed to delight in tormenting him.

One day Ludwig had a few coppers in his pocket. The evening before, he had played at the home of a wealthy woman in Bonn—one of those rare occasions which his father coveted for him so much. She had given him a purse with a few crowns, and as usual he had turned the money over to his father. In a spell of unusual liberality, Jan handed the boy a few coppers with which to buy sweets.

Ludwig was overcome at such unaccustomed generosity. He put the coppers in his pocket and began to plan how he would spend them the next day. What an orgy he would have!

The next morning, as soon as he had finished his practicing, he set out on his exciting errand. He walked into the little sweetshop on the Rheingasse and tried to look as if he were accustomed to buying candy every day.

"I will take some of the peppermint drops," he said importantly to the little old woman who kept the store, and put his hand in his pocket to draw out his coppers. They were not there.

He could not believe that he had lost them. Perhaps they were in another pocket. Just then, through the window, he caught a glimpse of Carl and Johann turning the corner. Was it his imagination that they were munching something—and that they had seen his dismay and were laughing behind his back?

An immense anger came over Ludwig. He ran after his two brothers as fast as his short legs would carry him, but didn't catch up with them until they reached their own doorstep. The boys had had time to decide what they should do. When Ludwig arrived, breathless as much from anger as from running, Carl hastened to him and put his arm around his neck. Ludwig was too spent to resist him.

"Little brother, don't be angry!" Carl winked slyly over his shoulder at Johann. "We were so hungry for sweets that we could not resist *borrowing* your coppers!" With a wheedling voice he pressed his arms closer about Ludwig's neck. "See—we have saved you a piece. . . ."

Ludwig's anger cooled. He had such a desire to be loved that his brothers could always get around him with a little coaxing.

CHAPTER IV

PRESENTATION AT COURT

(1 7 8 1)

THE CHIMES of the Münsterkirche were slowly ringing the noon hour. Ludwig always listened eagerly
for the joyous carillon that rang out each day at
twelve o'clock. But this time he did not stop to listen, for
he could hear the organ in the cathedral, and the music

drew him irresistibly out of the brilliant sunshine of the open square into the dim twilight of the church.

Half-hidden by the tall carved bench of the choir stall, he watched each movement of the organist with eager eyes. The light filtered through the stained-glass windows overhead and cast a soft pattern of color on the marble floor. Stately pillars disappeared into the dim obscurity above as if they were soaring upward on the waves of the organ's music.

For some time now Ludwig had been stealing into the church whenever he had a few moments to spare. One day an errand had taken him past the cathedral and he had heard the sound of the organ. For a moment he listened outside, then quietly pushed open the door and went in.

How wonderful to create music like that! Ludwig had played a few times on the wheezy old organ * in the church of St. Reginius, close to his house, but it did not sound like this. If only he might once try this majestic instrument!

The old organist was quite unconscious of his small listener and went on with his work, pulling out the stops, pressing on the deep-toned pedals, and using the two keyboards of the instrument. Occasionally, with a weary sigh he stopped to rest for a moment.

* Preserved in the Beethoven House at Bonn.

For fifty-odd years now Van den Eeden had been court organist to the Elector. He was growing old and stooped from his lifetime of hard work and could no longer sit so many hours without interruption. Today he stretched himself stiffly.

A timid hand touched his arm. He turned in surprise.

"Your Eminence—" a small voice faltered—"would you let me try the organ?" Ludwig trembled at his own boldness.

Van den Eeden looked at him in bewilderment. *"You!* Why, what might a child like you know about the organ?" His glance was not unfriendly; Ludwig took courage.

"I think I could manage—if you would let me try!"

The old organist threw back his head and laughed. "Of course—of course you could. Very simple!" he chuckled. "But I have no time for fooling. This new Mass must be ready for tomorrow." He looked anxiously at the difficult score in front of him.

The boy's face fell. He tried to explain to the old man how long he had been listening to the organ and hoping for a chance to try it, and how much all music meant to him. Van den Eeden was touched by his earnestness. He was a lonely old man, and his many duties as court organist and chamber musician could not make up to him for the lack of a home and children of his own. He looked

kindly and half-wistfully at the boy before him. Finally
he made way for him on the bench.

"Just for a moment, then!"

Ludwig was eager to prove his ability. He looked the
organ over carefully, located the different stops, and finally
turned to the open score before him and began to play it
from sight. It was hard for him to reach the pedals with
his short legs, but he managed after a fashion, and soon,
thrilled with the great volume of sound, he was letting
the organ swell in a perfect avalanche of music. The old
man listened in amazement.

"*Himmel,* child! What is your name?"

Ludwig flushed. "Ludwig van Beethoven, sir," he answered politely.

Old Van den Eeden gave a start and looked at him
more closely. "I should have known—you resemble him,"
he said with emotion. "Your grandfather, God rest his
soul, was one of my closest friends." He stroked his chin
thoughtfully. "If only I had time to give you lessons . . ."

Ludwig looked up at him with joyful gratitude. Van
den Eeden could not resist his pleading eyes.

"Perhaps a few minutes in the evening? We might manage that, eh?"

Night after night, the two met in the dark shadows of
the dim church and unraveled the mysteries of the great

organ. All through the day Ludwig looked forward to the moment when he could leave his cares and troubles behind him and steal into the vast obscurity of the cathedral. He missed the daytime brilliance of the radiant windows, but the peace and silence made him feel that he was entering into a different world—a world that he himself could fill with mighty harmonies.

Van den Eeden grew very much attached to the boy. Ludwig's quick understanding of the intricate organ, and above all his deep feeling for music, were a constant joy to the old man. But the lessons proved one more burden on old shoulders already near to the breaking point, and to Ludwig's sorrow, Van den Eeden was not able to continue long with his lessons.

Christian Gottlieb Neefe was appointed to succeed Van den Eeden as organist to the Elector. Fortunately for Ludwig, old Van den Eeden had spoken to Neefe about his gifted pupil, and Ludwig was able to continue his lessons with the new master.

Neefe was a composer of note and a musician of the highest order, but Ludwig found him a very different teacher from old Van den Eeden. He was strict and exacting and hard to please, and Ludwig missed the humor and kindliness of his former master.

"Now then," Neefe would say, "it is time you did some serious work. Enough of this silly tune-making. If you wish to be a really great musician you must study the works of Johann Sebastian Bach." Whenever Neefe spoke of Bach his voice became deep and impressive, and his eyes flashed. To him the great composer of the *Well-tempered Clavier* was like a god.

"But can't I have one little hour a day for writing melodies?" Ludwig asked.

Neefe's lip curled in a superior smile.

"Wait until you have studied composition more—learn the Preludes and Fugues by heart. Bach will teach you more than you could learn in a lifetime of tune-making!"

So Ludwig applied himself with a heavy heart to study what he feared would be dull and uninteresting. But the beauty and grandeur of Bach's music proved a revelation to the boy. He came to love it with a devotion that no other music ever surpassed in his heart.

Even the exacting Neefe was pleased with the diligence and speed that Ludwig showed in mastering his required work. By way of reward he set him a new task.

"Louis," he said (Neefe had spent some time at the court of France, and he had a way of changing the German names into French), "you have done so well with the *Well-tempered Clavier* that now I am going to let you compose some music of your own."

Ludwig's eyes shone. "May I show you some that I have already written down?" he asked eagerly. With mingled pride and misgiving he brought three sonatas to Neefe.

"So—you wish to be a composer!" his master exclaimed. "It is not so easy to write music!"

But as he looked through the sonatas his expression slowly changed. He saw that this boy's talent was far greater than he had at first suspected.

"Ludwig," he said solemnly, "you have a real gift. Some day you may be a composer . . . provided," he hastened to add, "that you are willing to apply yourself faithfully."

Ludwig assured him fervently that no effort would be too great for him.

Neefe turned the pages of the manuscript that the boy had brought him. "These sonatas, now, they are full of mistakes"—the boy looked downcast—"which is only to be expected, since you are so young and have not had much instruction." Suddenly an idea occurred to him, and he began to rub his chin in a way he had when thinking deeply.

Finally, he spoke again. "Ludwig, it is time the Elector took notice of you." The boy looked up with a question in his eyes.

"Max Friedrich is a good-hearted man—and he has a

pretty ambition for music. He wants to make Bonn one of the leading musical centers in Germany." Ludwig wondered what that had to do with his sonatas.

"Now, Max Friedrich loves praise. With a little wise flattery he could be favorably disposed toward you." Neefe smiled cannily. "Perhaps if we were to take these compositions of yours, polish them up a bit, and then inscribe them with a magnificent dedication to His Highness . . ."

Ludwig could not believe that his compositions were sufficiently worthy to lay at the feet of that great man, Archbishop of Cologne and Elector of the Empire. But Neefe knew what he was about.

It took some time to accomplish the necessary changes, and when that was done Ludwig had to copy his sonatas carefully, on fine white paper in his best and neatest hand. Last, but most important of all, came the dedication.

"Everything depends on that!" Neefe said solemnly, and they labored for hours over the masterpiece. Even Jan was called in to assist in the important composition.

At last they were satisfied with the result. Ludwig dipped his quill pen into the ink and began to copy the dedication with the utmost care:

Most Exalted!

Since my fourth year, music has taken first place among my youthful occupations. Thus early acquainted with the gracious Muse who tuned my soul to pure harmonies, I came to love her, and it has often seemed that she also loved me. I have now reached my eleventh year, and since then my Muse often whispers to me in inspired hours: "Try for once to write down the harmonies of thy soul!" Eleven years old, I thought—how would the role of composer become me? And what would the Men of Art perhaps say. Shyness almost overcame me. But my Muse desired it—I obeyed, and wrote.

And, Most Serene, may I now dare to lay the first fruits of my youthful efforts on the steps of Thy Throne? And may I hope that Thou wilt bestow on them with mild and fatherly eye Thy encouraging approval? The Arts and Sciences have indeed always found in Thee a wise Guardian and magnanimous Protector, and blossoming talent has prospered under Thy noble and fatherly care.

Imbued with this confidence, I take the courage to approach Thee with these youthful efforts. Receive them as a pure tribute of childlike reverence and with graciousness, Most Exalted, look down upon them and their youthful author!

Three Sonatas for Piano dedicated to the Most Reverend the Archbishop and Elector of Cologne, Maximilian Friedrich, my most gracious Sovereign, and made by Ludwig van Beethoven, aged eleven years.*

When all was finally in readiness, Neefe made arrangements to introduce the boy at court one evening when there was to be music.

* Ludwig was actually thirteen at the time, but his father, in order to make him appear more of a prodigy, had always given his age as two years

Ludwig was so impressed with the importance of the occasion that he almost became ill with anxiety and long hours of extra practice. Supposing he were to stumble in his playing—or that the Elector should not care for the sonatas he had so boldly dedicated to him? Ludwig felt that the entire future of his family and himself depended on this event, and as the time drew near he began to fear that he would never be able to go through with it.

"Don't worry, my child," his mother reassured him. "I know you won't fail."

Maria-Magdalena was the only one who remained calm through the excitement. Jan was in a fever of apprehension, and so anxious to have Ludwig appear well at court that he managed in some way or other to get the boy a new outfit for the occasion. Ludwig, who had scarcely ever before owned a decent suit of clothes, was greatly impressed by the magnificence of his new things. He would go to the cupboard a dozen times a day to inspect the beautiful satin coat with ruffles at the wrists, the black knee-breeches, and the large-buckled shoes. He imagined how wonderful he would look in all this finery.

Carl and Johann were openly jealous.

"What a misfortune to spoil that magnificent suit with a face like yours!" they sneered.

younger. Beethoven believed that he was born in 1772, but examination of the records has proved 1770 to be the correct date.

Ludwig knew that he was ugly. He had only to look in the mirror to see how his front teeth stuck out, how broad and flat his nose was, how sallow his pockmarked skin. At school, the boys called him *der Spanier* (the Spaniard), because of his dark complexion. No one realized how much his sensitive spirit suffered from the gibes that were thrust at his ugly face and unruly hair. He loved all beauty so passionately that it was a constant sorrow to feel himself out of harmony with the beautiful in Nature. In later years he partly overcame this feeling by forgetting about his looks or paying as little attention to them as possible.

At last the great day came. Ludwig was up at dawn and spent most of his time at the clavier in a final effort to perfect his playing. Maria-Magdalena begged him to spare himself.

"You will be too tired to play tonight!" she said gently to the anxious boy.

But Ludwig only looked at her with an absent-minded stare and went on feverishly with his practicing. He dressed himself hours ahead of time in his stiff and uncomfortable new clothes, and when finally Neefe called to take him to the palace, the boy was ready to drop with weariness and exhaustion.

"Remember, now, just how you must bow," Neefe prompted him. "And do not forget to smile at the ladies!" Ludwig kept moving his fingers up and down for fear they might become stiff.

"Be sure to speak loudly when you read the dedication," his master whispered in final warning as they were admitted to the palace by a gorgeously costumed flunky.

As they walked through the corridors of the palace, Ludwig forgot his anxiety for a time. The sumptuous furnishings and rich colors bewildered him with their splendor, and he felt as if he had stumbled into fairyland. When they were ushered into the great ballroom of the palace, he was blinded by the brilliance of the lights. In his poor home, where light was a luxury to be used as sparingly as possible, one or at most two candles were allowed, while here . . . ! Huge candelabra, of crystal that glittered like icicles, were filled with hundreds of burning tapers that flooded the hall with dazzling light. Magnificent mirrors and beautiful paintings lined the walls; delicately molded chairs, with brocaded tapestries and gilded traceries, looked to the boy as if they were carved in solid gold.

So did the clavier! In his wildest dreams he had never suspected that such a noble instrument could exist. He drew a deep breath of delight. . . .

Ludwig never forgot that first evening at the Elector's palace. Even in later years, when he played at the court of the Emperor, the memory of its magnificence remained undimmed.

A resplendent master of ceremonies moved to the center of the room.

"Most exalted Prince and Elector—gracious and noble lords and ladies," he cried in a loud voice, "you are to be entertained by a talented young pupil of Court Organist Neefe—Ludwig van Beethoven."

Ludwig looked up in terror: the dreaded moment had arrived. His fingers grew like ice, and he shook with fear. Neefe seized him firmly by the arm and whispered kindly in his ear: "Come, come, lad, this is no time to give way!"

Ludwig pulled himself together with a great effort, clutched his manuscript in his hand, and advanced to the thronelike dais where the Elector sat in state. He bowed with trembling knees and unrolling his parchment timidly began to read the dedication.

"Most Exalted—"

Max Friedrich leaned forward and put his hand to his ear. "What's that? Speak louder, I can't hear you!"

Ludwig looked up in startled apprehension. For a moment he was seized with such panic that he felt he must burst into tears and escape from the room. Then the determined spirit of his grandfather came to his rescue, and he began again in louder tones:

"Most Exalted! Since my fourth year, music has taken first place among my youthful occupations . . ."

When at length he had finished, Max Friedrich nodded gracious approval and directed Ludwig to play the sonatas for him. The boy was almost afraid to touch the glistening clavier, it seemed so fragile, but when he timidly struck a few notes and heard how clear and mellow they sounded —so different from the tone of his own poor instrument at home—he forgot everything in listening to his own playing.

"Bravo, bravo!" cried the Elector when Ludwig had finished. The boy's triumph was complete. Max Friedrich called him to his side and questioned him with interest about his work. Neefe explained eagerly how gifted Ludwig was and what remarkable progress he had made under his instruction.

"If you play the organ as well as you do the clavier," the Elector said as he laughingly pinched the boy's cheek, "we shall have to come and hear you one of these days."

Ludwig flushed with pleasure. He thought the old Elector was the most wonderful man he had ever seen, and he longed to serve him.

This was the first of many similar visits to the palace.

Max Friedrich often sent for the boy to play for him, and occasionally came into the church and listened to his progress on the organ.

It was a period of great happiness for Ludwig.

CHAPTER V

LUDWIG FINDS A FRIEND

(1782-86)

BEETHOVEN, you are a donkey!" The schoolmaster frowned at Ludwig over his spectacles. A titter ran through the schoolroom of Herr Krengel's Latin School on the Neugasse. Ludwig, his ears red, hunched sullenly over his desk. He looked distastefully around the stuffy room with its spotted walls and long, discolored

58

benches and desk. Who could learn anything in such an ugly place? He hated it deeply, violently, every board and crack and every grinning student in the room.

Just then the bell rang, and the students filed out as quickly as their strict German discipline would allow. Once outside, they formed a circle about Ludwig and began to dance around him. "Donkey . . . Sir Donkey! Shall we pull your ears for you?" they chanted.

Ludwig turned on them furiously. The boys were stronger than he was, but that made no difference. He felt that he must in some way avenge the months and years of insults that had been heaped on his head. He struck out blindly, with both hands and feet. It was the signal for a general fight. With a joyous whoop a dozen boys joined in, and Ludwig soon found himself at the bottom of a rapidly growing pile of kicking, scratching young savages.

They were too much occupied with the affair at hand to notice the approach of a tall, well-built young student from the *Gymnasium* (High School).

"Here now—what's going on?" cried a good-natured voice. A strong hand pulled off three or four of Ludwig's enemies. The rest beat a hasty retreat, and young Beethoven found himself alone on the battlefield. He sat up shamefacedly and rubbed the dust out of his eyes while the stranger helped him to his feet and brushed off his clothes.

"Not hurt, are you?" A laughing pair of blue eyes smiled down at him.

Ludwig looked gratefully up at his rescuer. He saw a boy some five years his senior, with a bundle of books under one arm and the student's cap of the Gymnasium on his head. He had a friendly expression and an open, honest countenance, and Ludwig was instantly attracted to him.

The lonely boy became suddenly conscious of a great need for companionship. He had always been so reserved that the other boys had kept away from him, and even the friendly ones had not been able to look beneath his hostile exterior and discover the sensitive, warm-hearted nature within. Ludwig longed for friendship and understanding, yet he was unable to overcome his natural shyness in order to reach out for them.

Franz Wegeler seemed so sympathetic that Ludwig found himself pouring out his troubles. He was ashamed to admit the reason for the fight. He tried to explain how difficult some of his studies were for him. "Latin, now— it's no use! I can't learn it."

Young Wegeler laughed good-naturedly. "Perhaps I could help you."

Ludwig was filled with gratitude. He felt that at last

he had found a friend. He longed to make a good impression on Franz.

"Come home with me," he said, holding out his hand impulsively, "and you shall see that I am no donkey at the clavier."

Franz returned with him to the wretched attic. He was filled with pity when he saw the disorder and poverty of the home. But when Ludwig sat down to play he was so amazed at the power and beauty that the boy was able to bring out of his poor instrument that the pity turned to admiration.

Each day after that, Franz on his way home from school would stop by for Ludwig. Then the two would take long walks through the fields together or else return to the attic for music.

For the first time in his life Ludwig had someone in whom he could confide and to whom he could tell the secret thoughts of his heart. The older boy helped him to improve his school work, but above all he brought him the sympathy and companionship he so greatly needed.

One morning when Ludwig had just finished his lesson with Neefe, his master turned suddenly to him.

"Ludwig," he said, "I have a new task for you. It will be a test—to see how well you have learned the composition lessons I have given you. Take this march by Dressler and write three variations on it. When it is finished, bring it to me, and we shall see what you have made of it."

Ludwig was not so happy about this sort of composition as he might have been. He much preferred "scratching his own tunes," but he made up his mind to perform his task so well that his master should be more than satisfied.

When the time limit that Neefe had set him was ended, Ludwig brought, not three variations on Dressler's march, but nine, all so cleverly worked out and so really musical in style that Neefe was astonished.

He was so impressed by his pupil's achievement that he arranged to have the variations published, and he sent an account of the boy's work to *Cramer's Magazine,* the leading musical journal of the day. This article was the earliest printed record of Beethoven's work.

. . . Louis van Beethoven, son of the tenor singer, a boy of eleven years * and of most promising talent. He plays the clavier very skillfully and with power, reads at sight very well, and, to put it in a nutshell, he plays chiefly the *Well-tempered Clavier* of Sebastian Bach, which Herr Neefe put into his hands. Whoever knows this collection of Preludes and Fugues in all the keys, which might almost be called the *ne plus ultra* of our art, will

* See footnote on page 51.

know what this means. So far as his duties permitted, Herr Neefe has also given him instruction in thoroughbass. He is now training him in composition and for his encouragement has had nine variations for the pianoforte, written by him on a march—by Ernst Christoph Dressler—engraved at Mannheim. This youthful genius is deserving of help to enable him to travel. He would surely become a second Wolfgang Amadeus Mozart were he to continue as he has begun.

Ludwig's eyes sparkled when he read the last two lines! To be able to travel, to see great cities and meet the world's finest musicians, perhaps even Mozart himself! How wonderful that would be! He began to build castles in the air.

But at that time there was no one in the little town of Bonn who was willing to help the boy in his career. He felt sadly discouraged at times, yet he never lost faith in the future. He continued to dream and look forward to the day when he should do great things.

One morning, some time later, Ludwig was a little late in coming to his lesson. He expected a reprimand, but instead of that, Neefe met him with a smile.

"My boy, I have been ordered to go to Münster with the Elector to play the organ for their spring festival. Someone will have to look after my work here while I am gone."

Ludwig listened with eager attention. Would Neefe by any chance let *him* take the responsibility?

The organist read his thoughts. "Yes, Louis, I think you could do it. . . ."

The boy's heart gave a leap. Here was an opportunity to show what he could do. He was willing to work all day and half the night if Neefe would really trust him with such an important responsibility.

Neefe could not have found a more conscientious substitute. Ludwig was always at the church long before the appointed hour; he could hardly tear himself away from the organ to go home to eat and sleep.

It was a queer sight to see such a young boy conducting the service at the organ. His legs were still so short that he had trouble in reaching the pedals. But he worked away with the greatest seriousness and played as if he were inspired.

He took advantage of this opportunity to improvise at the organ for hours at a time. More than one good citizen of Bonn would steal into the church to listen to the strange new music.

When Ludwig went home in the evening he would sit up late into the night working on a new composition. He wanted to surprise Neefe with it on his return, and prove to him by his diligence how much he appreciated the confidence which had been placed in him.

When Neefe came back he was more than pleased. "The Elector should reward you with a permanent position," he said, and, believing that Ludwig's faithful services should be recognized, he wrote out a petition to lay before Max Friedrich.

A few days later Ludwig hurried home with his head in the clouds.

"Mütterchen, Mütterchen!" he cried, dashing up the stairs three at a time. "Think what the Elector has done! He has made me Court Cembalist." Ludwig explained his new duties with great enthusiasm. "It means that I am to play the clavier in the orchestra and even to conduct when the regular leader is absent!"

Maria-Magdalena was overjoyed at his good fortune, but Carl and Johann were not impressed.

"What does *that* amount to?" said Johann. "Just wait until I am apothecary's assistant and we will have something to talk about."

"Yes," sneered his father, "but how much is the Elector going to *pay* you for all this?"

Poor Ludwig hung his head. He had been so overcome by the honor of his new position that he had not thought of anything else. But in those days honors were often considered sufficient reward in themselves. The boy found to his sorrow that he was still unable to help materially in relieving the distress of his family.

Maria-Magdalena put her arms tenderly about the boy's shoulders. She knew how he longed to help, how hard he worked, and what a heart of gold was hidden beneath his unattractive exterior.

Ludwig looked up at her gratefully. His mother was the one person in the world whom he loved with all the ardor of his passionate young heart.

"Darling Mother—*some* day I will earn enough to buy you everything your heart desires!"

When Ludwig was sixteen, a new sister came to the Beethoven family. Maria-Magdalena watched over the baby anxiously, for she had lost two little ones since Johann's birth, and she was terribly afraid that this child might be taken from her too.

Life was bitterly hard for Maria-Magdalena; she grew sadder and more colorless as the years went by, and her only comfort was in Ludwig's love and consideration. He longed to lift the burden from her frail shoulders, but there was so little that he could do! And now there would be another mouth to feed, one more care and responsibility for his mother—and for himself.

Conditions were going from bad to worse with the Beethovens. Jan paid little or no attention to his family and disgracefully neglected his duties as singer in the church. Had it not been for the high esteem in which Ludwig was held by the Elector, the father would long since have been discharged from his post. The family could never have existed but for Ludwig's meager earnings. He received practically nothing for his work as cembalist of the orchestra, but his occasional engagements to play at the palace or at the private home of some wealthy citizen helped to keep the wolf from the door.

Neefe, Ludwig's teacher, realized what a struggle the boy was having, and he finally went again to the Elector, Max Franz. Max Friedrich, who died in 1784, had been succeeded by his son.

"Your Highness," Neefe said, "Ludwig van Beethoven has served your orchestra as cembalist for several years, has he not?"

Max Franz admitted this to be true. "He is a gifted lad," he said complacently. "I have never known anyone to equal him—excepting, of course, the great Mozart."

"Then you have been satisfied with the way he has performed his duties?" Neefe asked.

The Elector had only praise for the boy. "He is so steady and reliable! No man could fill his place better."

"Then wouldn't it be possible to give him a real position?" Neefe went on to tell Max Franz about the dreadful poverty of the Beethovens, and how Ludwig had to be their main support.

"He deserves help," the Elector agreed. "The trouble is, the boy is still so young. All the musical posts are already filled by good men."

Neefe smiled. "I really need an assistant, Your Excellency. . . ."

The Elector thought it over. "Very well," he finally agreed. "Young Ludwig van Beethoven shall be appointed Assistant Court Organist."

The following week Ludwig was presented with a large, important-looking document in which it was stated that Ludwig van Beethoven had been created court organist, assistant to Christian Gottlieb Neefe, by order of His Highness Max Franz. A list of his duties was enclosed:

On all Sundays and regular festivals, High Mass at 11 A.M., and vespers at 3 (sometimes 4) P.M. The vespers will be sung throughout in Capellis Solemnibus by the musicians of the electoral court; the middle vespers will be sung by the court clergy and musicians chorally as far as the *Magnificat,* which will be performed musically. On all Wednesdays in Lent the *Miserere* will be sung by the chapel at 5 P.M., and on all Fridays the *Stabat Mater.* . . . Every day throughout the year two Masses will be read, the one at 9, the other at 11—on Sundays the latter at 10.

This time when Ludwig carried home the good news to his family, he was able to show tangible evidence of his promotion.

"Didn't I tell you that I would soon be earning more?" he cried triumphantly.

Jan's eyes fastened greedily on the gold coins, and Carl and Johann became suddenly very friendly.

Ludwig was agreeably warmed by their flattering attentions. "We shall have to celebrate, eh, Carl?" he said grandly. "What do you say, Johann, to an excursion down the Rhine?"

The brothers agreed with enthusiasm, and his mother looked at him affectionately. "Yes," she exclaimed, "you deserve a holiday, Ludwig!"

It had been years since Ludwig last went down the Rhine. He thought of his grandfather as they sailed slowly down the broad river; how proud old Ludwig would have been of his grandson's success!

They had their dinner at a little village and then walked

home across the fields. When they stopped for a rest, Ludwig wandered off by himself and stretched out beneath a giant oak.

He had been too ceaselessly employed these last years to go out into the open as he had done in his early childhood. But now, as he listened to the sweet voices of growing things around him, he felt once more the lure of Nature. He began to realize that solitude is necessary for all true creation. In the years to come he always found his greatest inspiration in the open—wandering through fields and forests.

CHAPTER VI

JOURNEY TO VIENNA

(1787)

EARLY IN 1787 Ludwig's friend Franz Wegeler went
to Vienna to study medicine, and from there he sent
back to Bonn glowing accounts of the gay life and
the many opportunities in the great city. "The concerts
here are marvelous!" he wrote. "Vienna seems to be the
Mecca for all the great musicians. Ludwig, old fellow, you
should be here! Can't you possibly come?"

Ludwig read the letter over and over. No one would

ever know how much he longed to go to Vienna, to see Franz, and to come into contact with that brotherhood of fellow musicians living in the metropolis. There were times when he thought he could no longer endure the narrow, stifling atmosphere of Bonn. The same trivial duties every day, the same uninteresting surroundings. He was bursting with ideas which he longed to express in music, yet somehow he could not get them into form. His mind needed awakening and stimulating. He realized too that he must have further study in counterpoint and harmony if he expected to go on with his composing, and there was no one in Bonn who could give him the necessary instruction.

Ludwig was nearly seventeen now, and he wondered how many years he would have to save from his meager salary before he could make the long and expensive trip to Vienna. Four years before, he recalled, Neefe had written: "This youthful genius is deserving of help to enable him to travel." Ludwig wondered if the Elector would now be willing to give him that help. Or, if that failed, perhaps he might be able to borrow the money for the trip. He was willing to mortgage his entire future if only he could get to Vienna.

Finally, though it is not known by just what means, the trip was at last made possible. Ludwig could hardly wait to tell his mother the good news. They were so close to each other, these two, that he felt sure she would be as happy as he was over his great opportunity.

But it proved a sad blow to Maria-Magdalena. The care of the little sister, added to the other hardships of her life, had weakened what strength remained to her. She had not told Ludwig of the pain in her side which was steadily growing worse. She didn't wish to alarm him, but the thought of losing the one who was dearest in the world to her was almost more than she could bear.

Ludwig stopped short in the midst of his glowing account. Maria-Magdalena had turned her head away to hide the tears which could not be kept back.

"Mütterchen!" he cried in surprise. "Surely you are not *weeping* at my good fortune?" He put his arms tenderly about her. Suddenly he noticed how pale and worn she was, and he remembered that lately he had often heard her coughing in the night.

"Perhaps I should not leave you." He looked at her anxiously. "No," he said bravely, "I cannot go!"

But Maria-Magdalena would not consent to such a sacrifice. "Yes, yes! You *must* go, child. I don't need you here. I have Carl and Johann—" she smiled with unconscious irony—"and besides, this cough is nothing. A little cold that will soon pass. I shall be better in no time!" She was pitifully eager to persuade him that all was well, for she realized how much the trip would mean to him.

Maria-Magdalena made a great effort to appear gay and strong during the days that followed, and Ludwig never knew how often her smile concealed a heavy heart and pain-racked body. Even her fits of coughing she made light of, and said they were due to dust, or choking, or whatever occurred to her at the moment. Ludwig was finally convinced by her good spirits that all was well and began joyfully to make his preparations for the journey.

What a wonderful time it was! Ludwig could hardly be blamed if his head was so high in the clouds that ordinary life ceased to exist. A trip in those days was an event of tremendous importance. There were no trains, no motor-driven vehicles. All traveling had to be done on horseback or by stage, and it took days and sometimes weeks to go from one place to another. It was a long and wearisome process, but Ludwig did not think of the discomforts he would encounter. To see new countries and new faces was a great adventure for this boy who had never been far from the small town of Bonn.

Carl and Johann were rebellious at their brother's good fortune. Why should Ludwig have everything? It wasn't fair, they said. And Ludwig wasn't quite comfortable about it himself. So when they begged for money—"since we can't have a fine trip, like yours"—he was only too ready to divide his meager savings.

When the time came for him to leave, Maria-Magdalena was afraid her courage would desert her. She clung pitifully to Ludwig, and he could scarcely bear to tear himself away. A sudden apprehension came over him like a warning, and at the last minute he would have given up his trip if his box had not already been strapped to the stagecoach.

But, once started, Ludwig forgot his misgivings in the excitement of the journey. He climbed to the top of the lumbering old coach where he could sit in the open and watch the country go by. The air seemed filled with lilting tunes. There was a song in each flower-spangled meadow, a symphony in the depths of every cool dark forest, and Ludwig felt an overpowering desire to interpret these things in music.

Ten weary days passed before he reached his destination, traveling during the daytime and sleeping at small inns by the wayside at night. He was possessed by the fear that he might lose the letter which the Elector had given him for Mozart. There would be little chance of gaining admittance to the master without this precious letter of introduction. Much depended on the interview! How terrible if he should fail to make a good impression!

When the last day of the journey dawned, Ludwig could

hardly wait to reach Vienna. The stagecoach, which at the beginning of the trip had appeared so swift to him, now seemed fairly to crawl, and he longed to jump out and run ahead, that he might get there sooner. As they neared the city, his excitement grew so great that it was hard for him to sit still in his seat. Miles before they actually arrived he believed they would get to their destination any minute; he thought himself in the very center of Vienna when they had but reached the outskirts. He could not realize, in spite of all he had heard, that a city could be so large. And when they actually arrived, he was overcome by the size of the buildings.

Vienna had not yet achieved the magnificence it was to attain in the later nineteenth century, but it was even then a rarely beautiful city, and the cultural center of Europe. To Ludwig it was like a scene from one of the plays he had occasionally attended at the little theater in Bonn, only much grander.

He was dazed by the crowds and noise; his sensitive ears could hardly endure the turmoil that beset him on every side. The streets were thronged with gay carriages and crowds of people. It was a city of terrible contrasts; extreme luxury and bitter poverty stood side by side, the one condescending, the other wretchedly envious. Ludwig, with his clear country eyes and strange insight, realized the deep injustice of conditions. He felt that a day would come when achievement and character should outbalance rank and worldly possessions.

Wolfgang Amadeus Mozart sat beside a table, his head buried in his hands. Before him was a litter of papers— bills from the tailor, from the grocer, from the butcher. He was everywhere acknowledged the leading artist of the day—one of the greatest musicians the world had ever known. Yet in spite of incessant work, his rewards were so small that he never seemed able to earn sufficient for his needs. Now he raised his head and said dismally, "It is no use, Constanze."

His wife was watching him sadly. He was extravagant, she realized, but so good, so generous to his friends. He would deny himself the necessary things of life if only he could entertain his friends as he felt they deserved. Yet he could never quite make both ends meet. Just when they began to get caught up, Constanze would fall ill again, and there would be more bills for doctors and medicines.

"The tailor, now—" Mozart went on in dejection— "perhaps we could cut down a little there." He looked up hopefully, then sighed again. "And yet—I must be well dressed when the Emperor commands me to appear at court!" He pushed the papers away and rose to his feet.

"These will have to wait. Lorenzo da Ponte is bringing a friend this afternoon to hear the music I am writing for his play, *Don Giovanni*. I think I hear them now." Constanze fluttered away to prepare for the illustrious poet and his friend, while Mozart with a sigh shook his discouragement from his shoulders. It would never do to trouble his friends with a gloomy face, so he hid his anxiety with a smile and went in to greet Lorenzo.

As soon as Ludwig was settled at the modest inn to which he had been directed, he set out to present his letter.

He was a long time finding his way to Mozart's house. There were so many streets and such high houses in this vast city that he felt he would never learn his way about. When finally he reached the place and stood before the great man's door, he was almost afraid to mount the steps. What if Mozart would not receive him, or should decide that he had no special talent? How disappointed the Elector would be—and Ludwig's mother!

He stood a long time before the steps. Finally he gathered his courage together and resolutely lifted the knocker.

A manservant in livery opened the door. Though Mozart was always in debt, a footman was one luxury that he considered a necessity—for was it not right that his friends should be received in fitting style?

Ludwig produced his letter and asked for the master in a trembling voice. The footman told him to wait on a chair in the corridor. Close by he could hear the sound of voices and occasional laughter; one voice rather higher than the others stood out, and he heard it say:

"Another prodigy! A protégé of Max Franz, the Elector of Cologne. But I can't see him now. Fritz, tell him to come back some other time!"

Another voice broke in: "We're in no hurry, Wolfgang —we can wait. Why not see this young upstart and get it over with?"

Ludwig felt a lump in his throat. Things did not sound encouraging. He was tempted to leave, but his stubborn pride prevented him. Mozart had evidently heard so many young musicians that it would be hard to make an impression on him. But he made up his mind to show the master that he was no ordinary performer.

Presently the lackey returned and took the boy into a large and—as it seemed to Ludwig—sumptuously furnished room. At one end stood the piano, an unusually fine instrument for that period. Ludwig, however, saw nothing but the slight, elegantly dressed man in satin coat and powdered wig who came toward him.

"His Highness writes that you are a musician of ability." Mozart spoke kindly, but Ludwig could see that he was not much interested. He looked at the letter again and read from its pages: ". . . also Ludwig van Beethoven has composed in a manner both original and deserving the recognition of so great a musician as your—" Mozart broke off with a cough. "I shall be glad to hear you play, young man."

Ludwig hardly knew how he reached the piano. To begin with, he was worn out from his long journey and the excitement of so many new and important events. Then the indifference of the master had a paralyzing effect on him and made him more shy and silent than usual.

At best Ludwig was not attractive to strangers. His features were irregular and undistinguished, his skin sallow and pockmarked, and his hair, in spite of all efforts, never looked as if it had been combed. His clothes were shabby and coarse; he had not been able to procure new ones, since he had given his money to Carl and Johann. The contrast between his clumsy, roughly clad figure and the elegant Mozart was sadly marked.

Out of the confusion that filled the boy's mind only one thought emerged. He had learned through his limited experience with composers that they usually preferred their own compositions; so in his desire to please Mozart he started at once with the master's music. But Mozart did not seem interested. He was different from other composers in many ways. Not only was he modest about his work, but so many young musicians had tried to flatter him by playing his compositions that it was the surest way to bore him.

He began to fidget in his chair. Then he rose and walked about, examining the pictures on the walls, and looked longingly toward the next room where his friends were waiting for him.

Ludwig could not help noticing the master's inattention. He redoubled his efforts and played a number of Mozart's most difficult compositions. But it was no use. Mozart had heard as much from other aspiring young players. Finally, in desperation, Ludwig stopped short and turned timidly:

"Will the master allow me to improvise? Perhaps be good enough to give me a theme?"

Mozart hesitated in his walk about the room and looked the boy over. Was the lad really worth bothering with, or should he make some excuse and dismiss him? At length he decided to give him a trial. He sat down at the piano and played a short melody that sounded simple enough. But within it was hidden a countertheme which only a clever musician would be likely to notice.

Young Beethoven recognized this instantly. Here, he saw,

was his chance to do himself credit. With intense concentration he threw all his powers into the improvisation, and developed and elaborated the theme and countertheme until Mozart himself was bewildered.

As the music increased in brilliance, the master became more and more astonished. He realized at last that here was something greater than he had ever heard before. He came and stood beside the boy and watched him with close attention. Finally, unable to control his enthusiasm longer, he went to the door of the next room and called to his friends:

"Lorenzo, do you hear what this boy is doing?" He shook his head significantly. "Pay attention to him. He will make a noise in the world some day!"

It was a great moment for Ludwig. Mozart was lavish in his praise. He called Constanze and his friends into the room and made the boy begin all over again so that they might hear him. He insisted that he remain to hear the reading of Lorenzo's *Don Giovanni* and the music that Mozart was composing for the new opera. Ludwig was delighted with the music but disappointed in the play; he felt that Mozart was lowering the high standards of his art by using it on such a frivolous subject.

Finally, as a climax to all this good fortune, Mozart invited him to go with them to hear the famous *Marriage of Figaro*. When Ludwig got into his hard bed at the inn that night, he felt that at last the gates of fortune were opened wide before him.

The next few days passed like a dream. Mozart broke into his precious time to give Ludwig lessons, and introduced him to many of the leading musicians of Vienna. There were wonderful concerts to hear, and strange new sights to see, and altogether the boy felt himself in a new and exciting world.

He was fascinated with the brilliant life around him. After the narrow and restricted customs of Bonn, the very air of this gay city was stimulating. Each day he was seized with a new inspiration and could hardly wait to carry it to Mozart for his approval.

There was only one disappointment. Franz Wegeler, whom Ludwig had specially wished to see, was away from Vienna at that time. But he would be back before long, and Ludwig looked forward with keen anticipation to his return. Then, if only his mother and little sister could be there, his happiness would be complete.

"Perhaps," he thought, "I'll be able to earn some money and send for them!" He hoped that he would never again have to go back to Bonn.

In those days letters were a long time in traveling from one place to another, and Ludwig waited anxiously for news from home. He was still a little uneasy about his mother's health, and he longed to hear that she was once more strong and well.

On his return to the inn one evening a few weeks after his arrival in Vienna, Ludwig at last found the long expected letter from home. He tore it open quickly, and the face of his beloved mother rose before him. But the letter was not written by Maria-Magdalena. It was from his father—only a few wavering lines, saying that his mother was very ill. She was not expected to live much longer. He must return at once. . . .

Ludwig sat with the letter in his hand, staring at it stupidly. Finally he roused himself and hurried to the stagecoach office to find out how soon he could start for Bonn.

CHAPTER VII

THE BREUNINGS

(1788-90)

LUDWIG'S JOURNEY back to Bonn was like a nightmare. All of his dreams lay shattered about him, but he was so torn with anxiety about his mother that he couldn't even think of his disappointment at having to leave Vienna.

The days that followed were dark with tragedy. Carl, through his indolence, had lost his position; Johann was too young to find work, and there was no money to buy the necessary comforts for the dying mother. The situation was desperate. Ludwig felt that his pride must no longer stand in the way; if necessary, he would beg in the streets to relieve his mother.

At last he thought of an old neighbor and friend, Franz Ries, and turned to him for assistance. It was the hardest thing he had ever done.

"If you can let me have the money, sir, I will repay it some day—on my honor!"

Ries knew the boy's character. "I am sure you will. Take it with God's blessing!"

Ludwig never forgot the debt. Years later, when Ries's son Ferdinand came to Vienna, penniless and without friends, Beethoven took the boy under his protection and treated him like his own son.

Thanks to the loan from Ries, it was possible to make Maria-Magdalena's remaining days a little easier, and when she closed her eyes for the last time it was not necessary to put her to rest in the paupers' field, as Ludwig had so greatly feared.

Throughout the mother's illness, Jan had seemed utterly crushed and out of his senses. He was not really a bad man at heart; in spite of his constant neglect of her, he had loved his wife with all the devotion of which he was capable. But he was too weak and selfish, too broken by years of dissipation, to help her when she needed it the most. Ludwig found himself responsible not only for the support of the family, but for the direction of his brothers and the care of his father as well.

He could not keep Jan away from the tavern. After Maria-Magdalena's death the father seemed to care for nothing but to sit in a corner at the inn, drinking and mumbling to himself.

Jan was paid a small yearly pension by the Elector, nominally in recognition of his past services as court musician, but really because of the high esteem in which his father, old Ludwig, had been held and the regard that the present Elector, Max Franz, felt for young Ludwig.

As long as Jan received the money from his pension, he was sure to spend it on drink. Ludwig finally decided that the only thing to be done was to ask the Elector to pay over part of the pension directly to him instead of to his father.

It hurt his pride terribly to explain the reasons for his request. In spite of Jan's dissipation, Ludwig loved his father and was loyal to him. He didn't realize that everyone in the town understood the situation, and both pitied and respected the unfortunate boy.

There was only one compensation in all the sorrow and

darkness of that sad time, and that was Ludwig's love for the little sister. He had always been devoted to her, but now she came to fill his heart with a tenderness undreamed of. She was so small and helpless, so dependent on his love and care! He felt like a father to her, especially since her own father was so indifferent. Ludwig tried to make up to the child for the loss of the mother whose absence she could not understand.

He would hurry home to her after his work was done. During the interminable day, while he was plodding through the church services (the Elector had been good enough to give him back his old position), or giving lessons to the fashionable young ladies of Bonn (and how he detested teaching!), he would look forward to the evenings when he could run up the stairs and be greeted by the little one's merry laughter and first stumbling words. Even this affection, however, was soon taken from him. Before the year was out, the little sister had gone to join her mother, and Ludwig was left utterly desolate.

Ludwig now felt his heart so empty and his life so intolerably lonely that he often wondered how he could endure it. Even his work ceased to interest him, and the future stretched out in an endless succession of dismal days. If he had not met the Breunings just at that time, he might never have recovered from his despair.

Herr von Breuning had been Councilor to the Elector some years before, and had lost his life in a vain attempt to save some of the state records when the palace of Max Franz burned down. At his death his widow and four children had left Bonn and gone abroad. For years now their house on the Münster Platz had been standing empty, and the gardens surrounding it were sadly overgrown and neglected.

Ludwig often passed by the place on his way to the cathedral. He always looked with longing at the trees that the walls enclosed, and when one day he discovered a break in the wall, hidden by an overhanging branch, he could not resist exploring. He never saw anyone there, and gradually the place came to seem as if it belonged to him. He had no time now to wander through the fields, but whenever he could spare a few moments from his many duties, he would steal into the Breunings' garden and find there a little of the peace and inspiration which Nature always brought to him.

One corner of the garden, close to the break in the wall, seemed particularly his own. It became his place of refuge when life grew too unbearable. He could even forget a little of his unhappiness when he sat in that still place, and felt himself one with the growing things around him.

One day late in September, when the leaves of the trees were turning to pale gold, Ludwig climbed into his garden with heavy feet and a heavier heart. Of late he had been too much occupied during his mother's illness, and afterwards with the care of the little sister, to seek out his favorite spot. But now that he was left alone, he turned once more to the only consolation that was left to him.

He was so engrossed in his grief that he failed to notice a change in the garden. The leaves had been raked from the paths, the flower beds weeded and filled with fresh blooms, and everywhere there were signs of renewed care.

But Ludwig was blind to everything but the sorrow in his heart. For once his secret garden failed to bring its accustomed comfort. As he thought of his mother and little sister, his father's shame and his own loneliness, he was seized with intolerable despair. Life was too great a burden! He longed to end it all. He buried his head in his hands and shook with racking sobs.

All at once there were footsteps close beside him. A gentle hand touched his shoulder.

"What is the trouble, my child? Can I help you?"

Ludwig turned with a start. He had never dreamed that anyone would find him in this unfrequented spot, and he was startled and also a little resentful at being disturbed.

But when he saw the friendly face of the lady bending over him, his anger vanished, and he rose apologetically to his feet.

"It is nothing, *gnädige Frau!* I thought I was alone—no one near. . . ." He wondered who this kind stranger was. What could she be doing here, in this forsaken garden? Suddenly he recalled that he had heard rumors of the Breunings' return; he had not paid much attention to these, for so many such reports had proved false. But supposing it was true this time! Could this possibly be Frau von Breuning herself?

At once Ludwig became painfully conscious of his untidy appearance and tear-stained face, and—worst of all—the fact that he was trespassing on private property.

"I have no right to be here!" he cried. "Will the gracious lady please forgive . . ." He tried to escape as quickly as possible, but she caught him by the arm.

"No, no, you shall not go until you have told me what grieves you." The kindness in her voice was so unmistakable that Ludwig raised his eyes to hers, and he saw there such sympathy and understanding, so much that reminded him of his mother, that he felt his reserve melt away.

Hélène von Breuning had been deeply devoted to her husband, and when he had left her alone with four children to bring up, she had at first felt as if she could not live without him. But instead of allowing her sorrow to wreck her life, she had turned her love so completely on her children that a happier or more united family could not have been found in the Rhine valley.

Ludwig was greatly touched by Frau von Breuning's interest in him, and he felt moved to tell her of his unhappy life, and of the loss of his mother.

"She was such a good, loving mother to me—my best friend!" he said sadly, yet half the bitterness was gone when he could speak about it. "No one could be more fortunate than I when I was able to speak that sweet name, 'Mother,' and it was heard!" He sighed profoundly. "And to whom shall I ever say it now?"

Frau von Breuning laid her hand gently on the boy's arm. Who should know better than she what it meant to lose a loved one! Through her own sorrow she was able to understand the grief of others, and the lonely boy was gratefully conscious of her sympathy.

The sun was setting in a mist of golden leaves before Ludwig had finished his story. He was full of remorse to think that he had kept the kind lady so long.

"I didn't realize it was so late! Forgive me for keeping you here like this!"

Frau von Breuning smiled in the indulgent way her children loved.

"I shall forgive you only if you will come with me into the house and stay with us for supper!"

Ludwig bowed ceremoniously, flushed with pleasure. What a blessed change it would be from the cheerless meal at home, so empty now save for sad memories!

As they walked toward the house Frau von Breuning told him about her children. There were four of them—Christoph, Stephan, Lenz (the youngest), and Eleonore, whom they called Lorchen. She was the only daughter, and the pride of the whole family with her gentle nature and sweet, merry ways. Ludwig, as he listened, pictured his own little sister, grown to gracious girlhood. . . .

And as they drew near the spacious old house, he could hear the sound of cheerful laughter. The last rays of the sun shone on the broad gray stone steps leading up to the house, bordered on either side with flaming chrysanthemums. Ludwig, glancing up, thought he must be seeing a vision, or else the happy inspiration for some vivid painting. At the top of the steps stood Lorchen, her golden braids flying, her blue eyes sparkling and her cheeks flushed with roses.

"Ah, there you are, *Mütterchen!*" she cried. "We wondered what had become of you!" She stopped short as she caught sight of Ludwig.

"This is a prisoner I have captured!" called Frau von Breuning gaily, holding fast to Ludwig, who was inclined to run away. "And only think, Lorchen, he is a musician—he has promised to play for us. Isn't it splendid?" She was so out of breath with her climb and laughing effort to retain Ludwig that she could hardly speak.

Lorchen met them halfway down the steps, and immediately began to bombard Ludwig with questions. What did he play? . . . Could he improvise? . . . Had he ever heard Mozart? . . . Ludwig was so bewildered by her gay chatter that he forgot his timidity, and was soon laughing and talking with the two strangers as if he had always known them.

In a few moments they were joined by Lorchen's brothers, and Ludwig's natural reserve returned until he discovered how friendly and unaffected they were. His heart warmed to the kindly spirit of these new friends, and his deep despondency began to lift a little.

Stephan took an instant liking to Ludwig. "You must see the dogs," he began, then interrupted himself to turn to his mother. "I'm forgetting to tell you that we have another visitor." Ludwig drew back. "Franz has come from Vienna for a short vacation."

Franz . . . ? Ludwig listened closely. Surely Stephan could not mean Franz Wegeler? Ludwig had not written to him since his return to Bonn—he had been too sad, too heavy-hearted for letter writing.

Then he heard a well-remembered voice calling to Frau

von Breuning, and before he had time to think, Franz Wegeler himself was striding down the pathway. Ludwig's surprise and joy were almost as great as those of Franz, who was amazed to find him there, apparently an old friend of the Breunings.

"I thought my good friends had not been back to Bonn for years," he said.

Then Frau von Breuning had to explain how the meeting with Ludwig had taken place, and Franz for the first time heard the sad news of Ludwig's bereavement.

Gradually Ludwig forgot a little of his troubles. His joy at seeing Franz and the sympathy of these new friends helped to ease the loneliness in his aching heart.

A merry party sat down to supper at Frau von Breuning's that evening. Ludwig's eyes opened wide with wonder and admiration as he saw the snowy damask and shining silverware. At first he felt strange and awkward and realized how crude his manners were. But before long he was too much interested in the merry conversation around the table to worry about himself. By the time supper was ended he had been taken in as one of the family. Those who knew Ludwig in his daily life, with his reserved and gloomy manner, would not have recognized him in the laughing boy who sat at Frau von Breuning's table.

Franz had much to tell them about Ludwig's music. They could hardly wait until the end of supper to lead him to the pianoforte.

And what a joy it was to play for these dear people! They were so appreciative. Stephan assured him that he played much better than the famous Haydn. "And I have heard him, you know, at Esterház, several times."

Lorchen sat on a little footstool near the piano. She couldn't find words to express her delight, and Ludwig thought he had never seen anything so lovely as this charming maiden.

After the music they sat around the lamp in the library, and Christoph read to them. It was the custom of the Breunings to spend an hour or two each evening reading the classics aloud. They were especially fond of poetry, and Ludwig, who had never had time in his busy life to become even slightly acquainted with the poets, found a whole new world opening up before him.

> "Truth exists for the wise,
> Beauty for a feeling heart.
> They belong to each other,"

read Christoph slowly. It was like a new harmony—the rhythm of the verses—the melodious words. Ludwig came to see that poetry is but another form of music. And when Lorchen read, he didn't know which was better, to listen to her sweet voice, or to watch the expression of her beautiful, delicate features.

Thereafter, life in Bonn was no longer so unbearable to Ludwig. He still had his brothers to look after and his father to care for, but much of his time was spent with the Breunings.

Their friendship and the fine ideals of the cultured home proved an influence which left a lasting mark on Beethoven's character. Gradually Frau von Breuning helped him to smooth out some of the uncouth angles of his nature, and while she was never able to conquer his wild temper entirely, yet it was thanks to her wise help that he learned to control it to a certain degree.

She realized that the very power that made him so violent would be a force that he could use in his music; and when he had queer spells, moments of oblivion to all around him—days when he would forget to go to his lessons and neglect his pupils—she would laugh gently and say, "We must not mind—it is his 'raptus' that has come over him!"

It was due to Frau von Breuning's influence and understanding that Ludwig was able to keep his pupils in spite of his erratic ways. She had him come to her home twice a week to teach Lorchen and Lenz. Lorchen was not a very serious student, but Ludwig forgave her everything for the pleasure of watching her white fingers fluttering over the keys. He would look at her starry blue eyes and rose-petal cheeks and think to himself that they were like flowers blossoming under the sunshine of her hair. There were times when he hardly knew whether she was playing Händel or five-finger exercises.

Frau von Breuning always insisted that he stay with them for supper after the lessons. Frequently he even spent the night there, when their reading lasted until late in the evening.

Hélène von Breuning was like a mother to him. And Lorchen . . . ? Ludwig scarcely dared ask himself that question.

CHAPTER VIII

FAREWELL TO BONN

(1792)

His Gracious Highness desires that the cembalist Ludwig van Beethoven shall appear as principal soloist in the entertainment to be given in honor of His Excellency, the Count Ferdinand von Waldstein. . . .

LUDWIG had heard a number of rumors about this Count von Waldstein. He was said to belong to one of the noblest families in Austria; he was fabulously rich, and—more important in Ludwig's eyes—he was an excellent musician.

When Ludwig began to play at the palace that evening, as usual he forgot everything but the music. After his poor, broken-down instrument at home it was always a joy to play on the palace pianoforte. The music had such a different sound that he could hardly believe that it came from his own fingers. He felt as if it were pouring directly into the air without conscious volition on his part. Now, as he lost himself in the music, he gradually passed from the set compositions he had started to play, and began to improvise.

Count von Waldstein had never heard such music. The Elector had told him about young Beethoven, but he was hardly prepared for such remarkable talent. Finally he came over to the piano, and leaning his arms upon it, he watched the young musician with deep concentration. Ludwig, suddenly conscious of his presence, was surprised to note the enthusiasm in the man's eyes. Such a friendly smile lit up his face that the boy felt singularly drawn to him. He was astonished to find the illustrious Count so much younger than he had expected.

"What was that you were playing?" Waldstein asked kindly.

When Ludwig, blushing, told him how he had forgotten himself and was letting his imagination direct his fingers, the Count was still more impressed. "It is a great gift, to be able to improvise like that!" he said, sitting down beside him. The Elector nodded with pleasure when he saw what an impression Ludwig was making on his distinguished guest.

"Yes," Waldstein went on, "in Vienna a musician's ability is judged by his improvising. Will you show me what you can do with this theme? It happens to be a favorite of mine. . . ."

Young Beethoven threw himself whole-heartedly into the task. He wove the slender theme into a succession of fascinating variations, and Waldstein became so enthusiastic that he finally burst into applause.

"Bravo—that was magnificent! Some day," he added, "you must write that down for me."

Ludwig and Count von Waldstein soon became close friends. To the young musician, the Count was the embodiment of everything that was attractive and desirable. While the boy's proud spirit refused to acknowledge another as superior simply because he possessed worldly goods (and Ludwig was inclined to be too proud in that respect), yet with the Count he felt that the difference in their positions was partly bridged over by their common love for music. Count von Waldstein on his side recognized the boy's genius and longed to help him.

Ludwig was too proud to invite his new friend to the humble attic where he lived. He could not bear to have him know the poverty of his unfortunate home. Waldstein had heard of the brave struggle that the young musician was making in his effort to support the family, and he determined to learn how Ludwig fared at home.

One morning, the Count went to the Rheingasse, where he had been told he would find the Beethovens. After searching for some time, he located the number, 934, a small unpretentious house crowded among others equally ill-favored. He inquired of Herr Fischer, the baker below, and was directed up the stairs to the attic. He could hear the sound of Ludwig's piano as he mounted the stairs, but he was not prepared for the scene of destitution and disorder that met his eyes as he softly pushed open the door.

The room seemed only half lighted by its small, deep-set windows. In one corner, bending over a decrepit, worn-out piano, Ludwig was straining to read from one of his manuscripts. Already the years of labor in this ill-lighted place had left their mark on his eyes. In later life he was never able to work at night, and frequently through the day would have to stop in the midst of his writing to rest his tired eyes.

Everything in the room was in disorder. During Maria-Magdalena's lifetime she had been so worn by hardship and her husband's selfish neglect that she had never had strength enough to keep things straightened up. It was an unfortunate influence for Ludwig. He became so accustomed to living in a state of confusion that the habit remained with him all through his life.

There were no cupboards for his music, so it was strewn about the floor. Most of it was written in the boy's own hand, for he could not afford to buy printed music, and whenever anything interested him or was necessary for his studies, he had to copy it off himself. Everything about him was old and dilapidated; Count von Waldstein's heart ached at finding a boy with such great gifts obliged to live in surroundings like these.

Ludwig sprang to his feet in confusion when he saw the Count enter the room.

"I came because I wanted to hear you play again," the latter explained.

Ludwig hesitated a moment. "I should be only too glad! It would be the greatest privilege to play for you, sir—" he hardly knew how to explain—"but this pianoforte"—he blushed awkwardly—"it is not so good! I am afraid it won't make such music as you are accustomed to hear."

Waldstein interrupted him with a smile.

"Your music would sound well on any instrument," he said kindly.

Ludwig tried his best to overcome the defects of his decrepit pianoforte, and the Count was almost able to forget the miserable tone of the old instrument in his wonder at the boy's art. But he saw how sadly handicapped he was.

He came over and stood beside the piano and waited until Ludwig paused for a moment's inspiration.

"Ludwig," he said, glancing around the shabby room, "I can see that there are many things which you lack and must need. Let me help you." He put his hand in his pocket to reach for his purse.

But Ludwig drew back in great offense. He was willing and glad to take money that he had earned, but charity he would not accept. Waldstein understood. He appreciated the boy's spirit and thought still more highly of him.

A few days later, while Ludwig was busily at work, he heard a commotion below. His brother Carl rushed into the room.

"Ludwig! A package for you—but *such* a package!"

From the stairs came a heavy tramping, scuffling sound. Ludwig rushed to the door and nearly collided with two men who were staggering under the weight of an enormous box. Or was it—? Ludwig caught his breath—yes, it was a piano, a wonderful new pianoforte.

"Herr Ludwig van Beethoven?" one of the men asked. "His Excellency the Count von Waldstein ordered this sent to you."

Ludwig was speechless with delight. Tears of joy stood in his eyes. What a wonderful friend he had! His happiness in possessing such a friend was as great as his appreciation of the splendid gift.

He tried to think of some way that he could repay the generous Count. Waldstein had suggested that he write down the theme he had given him, that first evening, together with the variations he had improvised. Ludwig set to work at once.

Two years later one of his first published works after going to Vienna was a set of "Variations on a theme by Count von Waldstein, for pianoforte, 4 hands." * And in 1805 Beethoven dedicated one of his finest sonatas to the man who had befriended him in those difficult early days.

Since the death of Mozart in 1791, Franz Joseph Haydn had ranked as the greatest composer of his day. Most of his life had been spent in the employ of Prince Esterházy, where, as leader of the Prince's private orchestra, he had been required to compose countless symphonies and

* Although published in 1794, before the Trios (Opus 1), this work did not receive an opus number until after Beethoven's death. It is listed as Opus 159.

chamber-music works. But in 1790 he left Esterházy's household and set out to see something of the world. After two years, spent mainly in England—where he wrote his famous oratorio *The Creation*—he returned to the Continent. On his way back to Vienna he planned to stop at Godesberg, only a few miles from Bonn.

Ludwig was beside himself when he heard that "Papa Haydn" was coming. His first impulse was to tell Lorchen. He hurried down the garden path to the little summerhouse where the girl sat with her sewing. It was seldom he had the good fortune to find her alone. One of the family was always there, or else Franz Wegeler. Franz was now a rising young physician in Bonn, and whenever he could spare a few moments he was sure to be at Lorchen's feet.

Ludwig threw himself down on the seat beside the girl.

"You could never guess who is coming!" he said importantly.

She looked up in laughing inquiry: "Some great person —the King himself?"

"Better than that," Ludwig exclaimed joyfully. *"Haydn!* Yes—Papa Haydn himself is coming to Godesberg next week."

Lorchen was properly impressed. Haydn had become so famous in England that everyone was anxious to see and, if possible, to hear him.

"Oh, Louis, what a chance for you!" She clasped her hands together. "If only Haydn will let you play for him! You must take some of your compositions to him. If they should meet with his approval, your fortune would be made!"

The musicians of the Elector's orchestra were in a high state of excitement over Haydn's visit. But when they heard that he was to remain only overnight, their hopes fell.

"We should give a concert in his honor," one of them suggested.

"How could we, when he is to be here such a short time?" another rejoined.

Ludwig thought carefully. There must be some way in which they could meet the great musician and show him their regard. "Perhaps the Elector will allow us to serenade him while he breakfasts."

The idea pleased Max Franz. Everything was decided, and the orchestra began to practice Haydn's compositions during every spare moment of their time.

On the eventful morning all the musicians rose at dawn and hurried out to Godesberg for the important occasion. Most of them had been playing Haydn's compositions for years, and the privilege of meeting the great man face to face was an exciting experience for them all.

Ludwig dressed himself with the greatest care, brushing his only good suit of clothes thoroughly and polishing his shoes with closest attention. For once even Frau von Breuning would not have been able to criticize his appearance! She was always begging him to be more careful of his clothes, but he lived in a world so far removed from such trivial concerns that he seldom troubled his mind about the way he looked—if only he was comfortable. But today he wanted to appear at his very best, so that he would make a favorable impression on Haydn.

The musicians filed silently into the large drawing-room of the Elector's country home. In an adjoining room Haydn was just sitting down to his breakfast. Suddenly the air was filled with music. He rose to his feet in surprise; the Elector threw open the doors between and disclosed the entire orchestra playing with rare enthusiasm one of Haydn's own celebrated compositions.

The famous musician had been fêted and complimented all over the land, but the simple kindliness and genuine appreciation of these Bonn musicians won his heart and moved him to a singular degree.

Ludwig watched him with adoration and listened carefully to every word the great man had to say. He was overcome with bashfulness and pleasure when the Elector chose him to sit beside Haydn at the elaborate breakfast which was served to the whole orchestra following the concert.

"Herr van Beethoven is our most promising musician," Max Franz told Haydn, and the latter asked kindly about Ludwig's work. The sincerity and force of the young man struck Haydn particularly, and after the breakfast he asked him to play.

"So—the lad has talent!" he remarked approvingly. "I hear that you write music as well. Have you any of your compositions with you?"

Ludwig blushingly produced the manuscript of a cantata he had recently composed. He felt that it was the best work he had done so far.

Haydn looked it over carefully. "It has great promise!" he said to the Elector. "With a little more knowledge of counterpoint, this young man could—well, he *might* accomplish big things!" He laughed genially. "You may be proud of him some day!"

The next morning Max Franz sent for Ludwig. He received him with unusual friendliness.

"Herr Haydn and I have had a long talk about your prospects, young man." He coughed self-consciously, as if all the credit belonged to him. "We think you have possibilities. . . . Well, the long and the short of it is— are you willing to work your hardest and really accomplish something if you have the opportunity?" He peered sharply at Ludwig; his regard for the boy had always been high, but he had never quite dared trust his own opinion to the extent of helping him financially.

Ludwig answered fervently: "Your honor, since Herr Haydn has so graciously approved my efforts, I feel now that I shall do really big things." His head was already full of masterpieces.

"Hold on!" said Max Franz. "Herr Haydn says that, unless you have a more thorough knowledge of counterpoint and composition, you will never get very far." Ludwig's face fell. He realized that this was his weak spot. With the exception of his few lessons with Mozart, he had never found a really adequate teacher in those difficult studies.

The Elector had a big surprise for young Beethoven. "We have decided to send you to Vienna, my boy," he announced. "Haydn will take you as a pupil; Count von Waldstein has graciously agreed to pay the expenses of your trip; and I—" he smiled with unusual geniality, "will continue your allowance—at least until we see what success you have."

Ludwig could hardly believe his ears. So much good fortune all at once! To have the recognition of the world's greatest composer, and on top of that a chance to get back to Vienna—the goal of his ambition! Then he thought of his father. Jan spent his entire time at the tavern now, drinking himself insensible. What would become of the miserable creature if *he* were to leave? And what of his brothers?

For a moment Ludwig felt all his high hopes dashed to the ground. Then a happy thought occurred to him: "When I get to Vienna I can probably sell some of my compositions and then I can send for Father and the boys to join me there."

Jan, however, never reached Vienna. He died shortly after his eldest son's departure. Ludwig was now relieved of one responsibility. But Carl and Johann continued to be a burden on him as long as he lived.

As the hour for Ludwig's departure approached, Bonn suddenly became very dear to him. How lonely he would be away from all his friends, he thought—and how he would miss the sympathy and companionship of the Breunings!

The day before he was to set out with the delegation from Cologne, Ludwig went over to bid them farewell. An air of mysterious gaiety seemed to hang over the household, and he had a quick vision of a flushed and laughing Lorchen dashing up the stairs.

"Lorchen!" he cried after her. But she only hurried the faster.

Ludwig was perplexed. He was so full of his own affairs and approaching journey that he could not believe his friends might have other concerns. When he went into the drawing-room the same atmosphere of excitement baffled his understanding. Frau von Breuning sat by the window, smiling secretly over her knitting, and barely noticed Ludwig's entrance. Standing by the chimney stood Franz Wegeler, looking very red and important, and Christoph and Stephan were clasping his hands and talking volubly.

There was a hush when Ludwig appeared. Then Franz cleared his throat and advanced with a self-conscious stride. "Congratulate me, dear fellow . . ." Ludwig stood petrified, a dreadful conviction growing on him. Franz continued exultantly: "Lorchen has just promised to marry me."

For a moment Ludwig was too stunned to speak. Then a wave of bitter resentment came over him. Was this, then, all that his precious friends thought of him! Here he had come to say good-by, wondering how he could live in Vienna away from them all, and they—they had already forgotten his existence. As for Lorchen—Ludwig could not bear to think of her. Resentful, hostile words rose to his

lips, and instead of the tender farewells he had expected
to take, he left his friends in a black rage.

The following morning, as he looked back at the vanishing city of Bonn, Ludwig's heart was filled with bitter
emotion. It seemed to him that everything he cared for had
been taken from him there—mother, sister, and now his
friends. . . . Only his music remained.

But as mile succeeded mile on the long journey to
Vienna, and the thought of his opportunities in the great
city grew on him, the past seemed imperceptibly to fade
away.

Now the future loomed ahead. He felt a new power
within himself—a power which his adversities had only
strengthened, and he dreamed of the great things he would
accomplish.

CHAPTER IX

EARLY TRIUMPHS IN VIENNA

(1 7 9 3)

V IENNA is quite music-mad," Papa Haydn told his
new pupil, Ludwig van Beethoven. "Of course,
not many people can afford large orchestras, like
Prince Esterházy, whom I served as Kapellmeister for so
many years, but most of the nobility retain at least a few
musicians, and some still insist that their servants must be

able to play various instruments so that they can make up an ensemble."

Young Beethoven's lip curled in disdain. That was like the nobility! Music was no more to them than a servant hired for their entertainment. But no one should ever dictate to *him*.

"Chamber music is very much in demand," Haydn continued. "I would advise you to try your hand at—say, some trios. Something not too difficult for amateurs to play," he added with a touch of irony. "It's the fashion among the nobility to be musical, you know. You should see how seriously they take themselves, these Counts and Princes—yes, and their ladies too—sawing away at their instruments as if they were first-class musicians. Their enthusiasm is amazing. Why, they'll get up at the crack of dawn to play together; sometimes they even ask to join the professional orchestras in public concerts!" He shrugged his shoulders. "But it's lucky for us composers that they think so much of music. Now if only you could get a wealthy patron . . ."

Ludwig soon found himself launched in the thick of Vienna's musical and social world. Prince Lichnowsky, one of the wealthiest men there and an ardent lover of music, took a great fancy to the young musician. Eventually he invited Ludwig to come and live at his house, and far from treating him as a servant—as Beethoven half feared at first—he showed him the greatest respect and consideration. He even went so far as to tell his valet that if he and Beethoven should ring at the same time, it was the musician who should first be served. Ludwig was so incensed when he heard of this that he proceeded to hire a servant of his own, though he could ill afford such an extravagance.

When Beethoven had completed his first compositions under Haydn's tutelage—a set of three trios for piano, violin, and 'cello (published in 1795 as Opus 1)—Prince Lichnowsky sent out invitations for a grand musical soirée.

One of the first to arrive at the party was Baron Zmeskall —tall, distinguished-looking, with hair graying at the temples, and almost as keen about music as the Prince himself. He played the 'cello, and he was very anxious to meet young Ludwig van Beethoven.

As the splendid drawing-room slowly filled with elegantly dressed guests, Zmeskall saw the Countess von Thun, mother of Princess Lichnowsky, settling herself in a high carved chair near the piano. He went over to the old lady and bowed low over her hand.

"I understand that our Prince's protégé is to play this evening," he said.

The Countess sniffed. "Yes," she answered curtly. "The Prince thinks this young Beethoven is a genius. But I can't understand what he sees in him. The boy is just an uncouth country yokel who doesn't even know how to behave in company."

Baron Zmeskall frowned. The old Countess, with her sharp tongue, was very different from her gentle daughter, the Prince's wife. She was forever finding fault with her son-in-law and criticizing the Prince's devotion to the arts.

"But everyone says that this fellow is remarkable," Zmeskall insisted. "Even Haydn admits that he has great possibilities. And that, you know, is a good deal for him to say."

The Countess tossed her head, and the plumes of her elaborate headdress quivered disdainfully. "He is a young upstart—moody—temperamental—no manners at all. Why, fancy," she went on in a shocked voice, "he cares no more for a prince than for a lackey! Nothing can induce him, for instance, to play if he doesn't feel in the humor. I myself got down on my knees to him one day, and still he would not play!"

Zmeskall smiled behind his hand. He could picture the scene: the eccentric old Countess with her ridiculous head-dress, kneeling before a furious young Beethoven who denied anyone's right to dictate to him.

"And that isn't all," the Countess grumbled. "Your fine young gentleman is not satisfied with our dinner hour! The other day he was walking in the garden, and I overheard him say, 'I can't stand the ceremony here. Every day I have to be back by three-thirty, put on a better suit, shave, and so on. Better go to a tavern and be independent.' "

Zmeskall laughed outright. "I've heard about his love of independence. He's a young rebel, this Louis van Beethoven. If it's not the customs of society he defies, it's the old set rules of music he delights in setting aside. But the Prince believes he will become an even greater composer than Haydn himself—"

"Sh—sh, here comes Haydn now," Countess von Thun interrupted. "Young Franz von Brunswick is with him. He is to play the 'cello with the trio this evening."

Papa Haydn was growing stout with the passing years, but instead of making him more genial it seemed only to add to his pompousness. He dressed always with the greatest elegance and was as careful with every detail of his appearance as he was particular about the way he wrote his music.

"Good evening, Excellency," Baron Zmeskall called as Haydn greeted the Countess with a flourish of his lace-trimmed handkerchief and a low bow. "We were just speaking of your young prodigy who has taken Vienna by storm."

Haydn smiled. "Well, he *is* a gifted fellow, this Beethoven, but he has strange ideas. You cannot imagine what a trial it is to teach him. He simply will not follow rules!"

Just then a hush swept over the company and two lackeys with powdered wigs threw open the doors to admit Prince Lichnowsky—resplendent in his bright court uniform—and his charming, sweet-faced wife. The Princess was an unusually cultured and tactful person. Beethoven was already devoted to her, and in later years she was the only person who could make the headstrong musician listen to reason.

Behind the Prince and Princess came a short, stocky figure with dark unruly hair and a swarthy face lit up by small, piercing black eyes. He was dressed with the utmost simplicity, his somber clothes being in marked contrast to the gay attire of the rest of the company.

Prince Lichnowsky turned to him with an affectionate gesture. He had been Beethoven's good angel ever since the boy had come to Vienna a year before, poor and unknown, and during the years that followed he never failed in his appreciation and support of the young musician.

As Beethoven moved towards the clavier there were whisperings on all sides and an audible sniff from the old Countess, but he was quite unconscious of the interest he provoked. Without a word to anyone he sat down and began to play—first softly, as if half dreaming, then louder and more triumphantly, until the audience forgot his plain, unattractive appearance and began to see that here was something quite out of the ordinary.

Haydn passed from group to group, curious to know what impression his pupil was making. "Yes," he told them, "he had much to learn when I took him. A country boy, you know." He went over to the piano with a roll of music in his hand.

"Louis!" he called, "I have just discovered an old manuscript by Bach. Will you play it for the Prince?"

The music was written in the great Johann Sebastian's own hand, and was so old and faded that it was difficult to tell what the notes were really meant to be. The musicians in the company pressed eagerly around the manuscript to examine it. Herr Förster, who was later to become one of Beethoven's good friends, shook his head dubiously.

"It will be almost impossible to decipher it!" he exclaimed.

Beethoven's eyes lit up as he took the music. He had a deep reverence for the great master's works, and Bach, even in manuscript, was an open book to him. To the surprise of everyone he played the composition with perfect ease.

A murmur ran through the audience, while even the musicians showed surprise. "Bravo!" cried Förster with a patronizing smile. "I couldn't have done it better myself."

He cleared his throat self-consciously and raised his voice a little. "The Prince begged me to bring the score of my new trio this evening. Perhaps you would like to play the piano part?" The last movement was so complicated that he felt sure this young upstart would not be able to get through it.

Beethoven took the music from Förster. "If you desire, I will play it," he said shortly.

The first violinist of Prince Lichnowsky's quartet and Franz van Brunswick began to tune their instruments, and with Beethoven at the piano they started the trio. After they had been playing a few moments, young Brunswick suddenly discovered that his part was incorrectly written. He frowned anxiously and looked closely at the score again. Beethoven noticed his predicament and took a quick glance at the music. "Play it thus," he whispered, humming the 'cello part while continuing with his own playing. The Count, quick to follow, caught up the melody and finished the trio brilliantly.

At the end of the performance, Brunswick questioned the young musician in amazement. "How did you know how my part ought to go?" he asked.

Beethoven seemed surprised. "It *had* to go that way, if Herr Förster knew anything about composition," he said with a bow in the direction of the other composer.

Förster was only too glad that the mistake had passed unnoticed by the rest of the company.

Count von Brunswick, who later became one of Beethoven's close friends, looked at the young composer with undisguised admiration.

"How on earth could you play the last part so fast?" he asked. "It must have been impossible for you to see the individual notes!"

Beethoven pondered a moment. "It is all in understanding the language of music," he answered simply. "You do not notice the details because you know the meaning of the whole."

Baron Zmeskall nodded in approval and turned towards the old Countess with an "I told you so" air.

Prince Lichnowsky now came forward. "Let us hear the three trios you have just composed," he said to Beethoven.

Haydn tapped his chin nervously. He feared the trios would not please the company. "Too modern for my taste!" he muttered to the Countess von Thun.

But in spite of his misgivings the compositions were received with enthusiasm. Prince Lichnowsky congratulated Beethoven with real feeling, and Count Rasumowsky, a tall, handsome Russian who was married to the Princess's sister, shook him warmly by the hand. "Put me down as a subscriber when you publish your trios," he said. "One of these days you will have to write some quartets for me." Zmeskall, too, wanted a copy of the trios. "My boy," he said earnestly, "you will console us for the loss of Mozart."

Haydn decided that his own judgment had been a little hasty. "Your trios are better than I expected," he said to Beethoven, "with the exception, perhaps, of the third. If I were you, I should not publish that one."

The younger musician looked at him in surprise. "Why, that is the very best one of all!"

"*You* may think so," Haydn exclaimed, "but I am not so sure. I see you have dedicated the trios to Prince Lichnowsky. However," he added, "I shall not object if you put 'Pupil of Haydn' on the title page."

Beethoven's quick temper began to rise. "Pupil of Haydn!" he exclaimed. "I think Your Honor has been too engrossed with his own compositions to pay much attention to his pupils!"

"Well, now!" the older composer exclaimed. "What sort of gratitude is this, young man? It's fortunate that I am leaving for England soon and you will not be burdened longer with my instructions. Perhaps Herr Albrechtsberger will find it easier to keep you to your tasks."

Haydn never quite forgave his arrogant young pupil. In 1801, after the first performance of Beethoven's *Prometheus,* the two met on the street.

"I heard your *Prometheus* yesterday," said Haydn affably. "It pleased me very much."

Beethoven could never resist a pun. Referring to Haydn's most celebrated work, he answered ironically, "That is very kind of you, dear Papa Haydn. But my music is hardly a 'Creation.'"

Haydn raised his eyebrows. "Quite true. It is not a creation—and what's more, I doubt if it ever will be!"

A few months later, Beethoven decided that he could no longer endure the restrictions of his life in Prince Lichnowsky's household. Better one room and freedom than a whole palace without independence!

One evening as he returned to his solitary lodgings, he suddenly began to think of the Breunings who had been so close to him in Bonn. It was a year now since he had left his native city, and in all those months he had not written to them. He had often wanted to send Lorchen a letter and beg her forgiveness for his miserable behavior at their last meeting, but somehow his stubborn pride always prevented. Tonight he made up his mind that he would write the long-delayed letter and try to make his peace with the family.

As he reached the doorstep of his lodgings, he saw a waiting figure.

"Ludwig!"

Beethoven rubbed his eyes. He thought for a moment that he must be still dreaming of the past, for there before him stood Lorchen's brother, Stephan von Breuning.

"Ludwig, old fellow—how are you?" Stephan clasped him warmly by the hand. "I have just arrived in Vienna on a visit, Ludwig, and you are the first person I have sought out."

Beethoven was filled with remorse. "How good of you, best of friends!" he exclaimed. "How generous of you to forget the past! It is unpardonable of me not to have written."

Breuning laughed. "We have forgotten all about that. In fact, I am filled with messages to you from all the family. You can't imagine how proud we are of your great success here. Why, Lenz—" he reached down into the pocket of his greatcoat—"Lenz made me promise to get your autograph in his album."

The floodgates of Beethoven's heart were opened. None of his new friends and admirers could take the place of the Breunings. To be sure, Carl and Johann had followed him to Vienna as soon as he was able to send them money for the journey, but they were more of a burden than a comfort to him. Stephan and Lenz had been much more like his own flesh and blood than had his own brothers. He began to realize how much he had missed the Breunings' companionship and counsel. In his anxiety to hear everything that had happened to each one of them during the past year, he plied Stephan with innumerable questions.

When Breuning finally left, it was far into the night. But Beethoven took no note of time. He sat down before his writing table and began a long letter to Lorchen:

MOST ESTIMABLE LEONORE! MY MOST PRECIOUS FRIEND!

Not until I have lived almost a year in the capital do you receive a letter from me, and yet you have most assuredly been perpetually in my liveliest memory. Often in thought I have conversed with you and your dear family, though not with that peace of mind which I could have desired. It was then that the wretched misunderstanding hovered before me and my conduct presented itself as most despicable. But it was too late. Oh, what would I not give could I obliterate from my life those actions so degrading to myself and so contrary to my character. . . . Your good and noble character, my dear friend, is sufficient assurance to me that you forgave me long ago. But we are told that the sincerest contrition consists in acknowledgment of our faults; and to do this has been my desire. . . .

With this you will receive a dedication from me to you concerning which I only wish that the work were a larger one and more worthy of you. I was plagued here to publish the little work, and I took advantage of the opportunity, my estimable E., to show my respect and friendship for you and my enduring memory of your family. Take this trifle and remember that it comes from a friend who respects you greatly. Oh, if it but gives you pleasure, my wishes will be completely fulfilled. Let it be a reminder of the time when I spent so many and such blessed hours at your home. Perhaps it will keep me in your recollection until I eventually return to you, which, it is true, is not likely to be soon. . . .

In conclusion I venture a request: I should like once again to be so happy as to own a waistcoat knit of hare's wool by your hands, my dear friend. Pardon the request, my dear friend, but it proceeds from a great predilection for everything that comes from your hands. Privately, I may also acknowledge that a little vanity is also involved in the request: I want to be able to say that I have something that was given me by the best and most estimable girl in Bonn. I still have the waistcoat which you were good enough to give me in Bonn, but it has grown so out of fashion that I can only treasure it in my wardrobe as something very precious because it came from you.

You would give me much pleasure if you were soon to rejoice me with a dear letter from yourself. If my letters should in any way please you I promise in this to be at your command so far as lies in my power, as everything is welcome to me which enables me to show how truly I am

Your admiring true friend,

L. v. BEETHOVEN

As he wrote the last words Beethoven noticed Lenz's album which Stephan had left on his table. For a moment he was lost in memories, and the picture of his first evening with the Breunings came back to him. Then slowly and with great care he wrote down the lines that Christoph had read aloud to them and which he had never forgotten:

> Truth exists for the wise,
> Beauty for a feeling heart.
> They belong to each other.

CHAPTER X

"HIS ROYAL HIGHNESS"

(1 7 9 8)

To His Well Well Highest and Bestborn, the Herr von Zmeskall, Imperial and Royal as also Royal and Imperial Court Secretary:

Will His High and Wellborn, His Herr von Zmeskall's Zmeskality have the kindness to say where we can speak to him tomorrow?

NICOLAUS ZMESKALL VON DOMANOVECZ was old enough to be Ludwig's father, but he took a great fancy to the boy, and the two soon became fast friends. Zmeskall was highly amused at the young musician's preposterous humor and queer fancies. Far from being offended by the absurd and often disrespectful notes that he was always sending him, the Baron carefully cherished these and laid them away.

After six years in Vienna, Ludwig van Beethoven had become celebrated. His rugged individualism and personal eccentricities, no less than his amazing skill at the piano and the originality of his compositions, all combined to build up a reputation that grew almost legendary as the years went by.

Although in 1798 he was still chiefly known as a piano virtuoso, Beethoven had already published a number of chamber-music works and some dozen pianoforte sonatas. When he left Prince Lichnowsky's household, Baron Zmeskall's home became the meeting place where the leading musicians of the city gathered to try over the rising young composer's works.

MY DEAREST BARON MUCKCARTDRIVER [Beethoven wrote]:
*Je vous suis bien obligé pour votre faiblesse de vos yeux.** Moreover I forbid you henceforth to rob me of the good humor into which I occasionally fall, for yesterday your Zmeskalldomanoveczian chatter made me melancholy. The devil take you; I want none of your moral [precepts], for Power is the morality of men who loom above the others, and it is also mine; and if you begin again today I'll torment you till you agree

*I am very much obliged to you for the weakness of your eyes.

that everything that I do is good and praiseworthy, for I am going to the Swan—the Ox would be preferable, yet this rests with your Zmeskallian Domanoveczian decision.

Adieu Baron Ba . . . ron, ron/nor/orn/rno/onr.

Beethoven chuckled under his breath and reread the letter with as much pride as if he had written a masterpiece. But the writing was not so clear as it might have been; the point of his goose-quill pen had grown so dull that it was past repairing. He looked regretfully at it and wondered if his friend would have some quills to send him.

Best of Music Counts! I beg you to send me one or a few pens, of which I am really in great need.

As soon as I learn where really good and admirable pens are to be found, I will buy some of them. I hope to see you at the Swan today.

Adieu, most precious
Music Count,
Yours, etc.

His Highness von Z. is commanded to hasten a bit with the plucking of his quills (among them, no doubt, some not his own). It is hoped that they may not be too tightly grown.

"Bah, it will not write at all!" he exclaimed in disgust, throwing down his pen. "And how shall I copy my new concerto now?"

Beethoven ran his fingers through his thick black hair and frowned impatiently. Finally he decided to deliver his note to the Baron in person and not wait for a messenger to bring the needed quills.

A few minutes later he was threading his way through the crowded streets of Vienna toward the Bürgerspital, where Baron von Zmeskall lived.

As soon as he started to walk in the fresh air, his mind, as usual, began to turn to music. The last movement of his new concerto was not yet clear to him. He hummed the theme under his breath. "No—not quite." He tried it again. "That's better. . . ." The sound grew louder. "Now I have it!" he cried joyfully, and began to wave his arms as if he were directing an orchestra.

The passers-by looked at him in amazement and began to shake their heads significantly. But he was no more conscious of them than if he had been out in the country, miles away from everyone.

An elderly man with a violin case tucked under one arm turned in surprise as he hurried past.

"Herr van Beethoven!" he exclaimed with delight. "What luck to run across you!"

Beethoven came back to earth and smiled with sudden pleasure.

"Why, Krumpholz, old fellow!" he said heartily. "You are just the person I need." He took him eagerly by the arm. "Do you remember the third movement of the new concerto I played for you the other day?" Krumpholz nodded vigorously. "I think I have the right theme at last for the finale." He hummed over the melody that had been developing in his mind as he walked along. Then he sketched a few lines in his notebook.

Krumpholz listened with admiration to the new theme. "Wonderful!" he said with enthusiasm. "You have hit it exactly!" He shook his head sadly. "To think that I have spent a lifetime trying to find one such melody. And you, a young man not yet thirty, can turn them out every day! Ah, that is genius!"

"Come, come, now!" Beethoven interrupted. "Would you turn my head? You remind me of a king's jester forever singing his master's praises! Come with me to Baron Zmeskall's home," he suggested. "I have urgent business there! You can help me," he continued mischievously, "to relieve His Zmeskallity of a few quills."

Krumpholz caught the joke and laughed with appreciation. Who but Beethoven would have dared to take such liberties with the dignified Baron?

Zmeskall, Franz von Brunswick, and young Ignatz Schuppanzigh—one of Vienna's best violinists—were just preparing to play a trio together when suddenly the door opened a crack and a shaggy black head was thrust through the opening. Beethoven had a way of appearing in this manner—a sort of reconnoiter to discover just who was present. If he saw someone whom he wished to avoid, he would retire as abruptly as he had arrived.

"I salute you!" he announced, advancing with extreme gravity and holding out his letter to the Baron. "Allow me to present a petition—something regarding quills. . . ."

Zmeskall read the note and clapped his young friend on the shoulder. "My dear Herr Music-Highness," he cried jovially, "you shall have all the pens my house contains—on condition that you give us some music in exchange!"

"I was just on my way to deliver a new composition to you, Milord Falstaff," Beethoven said, turning to Schuppanzigh with a twinkle in his eye. The little violinist, who was almost as broad as he was tall, waddled closer. "I hope it is a Scherzo," he exclaimed.

Beethoven drew from his pocket a roll of music carefully tied with a red ribbon and handed it to him. "No, it is a song this time. My latest masterpiece is dedicated to *you,* Herr Ignatz," he said impressively.

Schuppanzigh opened the music eagerly, but his expression changed when he read the inscription:

TO MY GREAT FRIEND, IGNATZ

"LOB AUF DEN DICKEN"

"Praise of the Fat One!" Zmeskall and Krumpholz roared with laughter. And so did Beethoven. There was nothing he loved better than a practical joke—at the expense of someone else. But if it happened to be turned on himself, he seldom took it with good grace.

"Let's hear your song," the Baron urged, holding out the manuscript.

Beethoven began to sing in a mournful bass. Krumpholz put his fingers in his ears. "Terrible!" he moaned. "Here, take my violin and play it instead."

The composer looked at him in pained surprise. "On the violin?" He shook his head lugubriously. "I never could get on with the violin." His friends thought he was joking again. In those days when every musician was expected to play several different instruments, it was not likely that the great Beethoven could be anything but a first-class violinist. Krumpholz forced the instrument into his hands with a laugh.

"Here, now, anything is better than that awful singing."

"Oh, well, you shall see!" Beethoven tucked the instrument under his chin and began to play vigorously.

"Ai . . . have mercy . . . !" Schuppanzigh shrieked. "In heaven's name, man, *stop!*" shouted Krumpholz. The room shook with harsh sounds, until finally Brunswick and the two violinists controlled their laughter long enough to wrest the instrument from him.

Beethoven pretended to be indignant. "My playing does not please you?" He struck an attitude of extreme resentment. "Perhaps *you* would like to teach me, Maestro Schuppanzigh?" Suddenly he was serious. "You should have heard the young violinist who played at Frau Constanze's last night. Now that was playing for you!—and a modest personality!" He looked pointedly at the "fat one." "I turned the pages for this young fellow with the best possible grace, but when he glanced up and saw me he seemed positively terror-stricken!"

Beethoven looked at himself inquiringly in a near-by mirror. "Am I such a devil of a fellow that my phiz scares people?"

Schuppanzigh saw a chance to get even. "Can you doubt it?" he asked mischievously.

Krumpholz hastened to reassure his friend.

"That was young Amenda you heard. If you only knew how he admires you!" Beethoven was not sure whether the older man was serious or not. "He really does," continued Krumpholz. "In fact, he has wanted to know you for a long time, Frau Mozart told me. But he has heard that you are a gruff old bear. And so—" he laughed— "I suppose when he saw you standing there turning the music for him, he expected you would eat him alive!"

Krumpholz dodged as Beethoven advanced with a roar.

"What nonsense you talk! Just for that you shall go yourself to the young man and tell him I am as meek as a newborn lamb. Gruff old bear . . ." he rumbled. "Do you hear, Herr Violinist? Go to Amenda immediately. Better still, bring him to me that I may correct such an erroneous impression." He placed one hand between the buttons of his waistcoat and drew himself up imposingly. "Tell him, pray, that His Royal Highness, Ludwig van Beethoven, requests that he rejoice him with his company."

"Herr Amenda, a visitor to see you!" Frau Constanze Mozart called to Carl Friedrich Amenda, who was giving her young daughter a lesson on the violin.

Amenda rose in surprise. Who could be calling on him at this hour? He had come to Vienna only recently, where, through the influence of Prince Lobkowitz, he had been engaged as music teacher in the family of Mozart's widow. Three years before, he had finished his theological studies at the University of Jena, but his love of music was so great that he had given up everything else in order to devote himself to the violin.

Krumpholz had met Amenda before, and he knew how the younger man worshiped Beethoven. "I have come with a message from the master," he said impressively.

"You don't mean—*Beethoven?*" Amenda faltered. He had long been an ardent admirer of the young composer, but he had heard too much about his peculiarities to dare seek his acquaintance.

To the younger men Beethoven had become a symbol of the new age. They esteemed him all the more highly because the older musicians criticized his compositions as too startling and original. Amenda admired every note that the young composer had written, and when, the previous evening, he had suddenly looked up and discovered Beethoven himself turning the pages for him, his confusion had been so great that he could not utter a word.

When Krumpholz told him what an impression he had made on his hero, Amenda could hardly believe his ears. All night he had been tormenting himself for being such a numskull the evening before.

"What have you done," Krumpholz exclaimed with a laugh, "to capture Beethoven's heart in this way?"

Amenda hurried at once to Beethoven's rooms and knocked timidly at the door. There was no reply. He tried again without result. With a final knock he was about to leave, when suddenly the door flew open and the master himself appeared. He was clad only in his undergarments, and was in the midst of shaving, his face covered with lather. But when he saw Amenda he exclaimed with pleasure.

"Ah, it is you!" he cried, and embraced him cordially.

Half of the lather transferred itself to Amenda's person, and they both laughed.

"Now, never mind. It will all wipe off—and I promise not to growl too loudly." Beethoven laughed and pressed Amenda into a rickety chair. "Just wait until I finish this tiresome business, and we shall have some music."

He stood before a small mirror near the window and continued his shaving without thought of the amusement his appearance caused the passers-by below.

"Such a bother . . ." he grumbled to himself. "I am no sooner shaved than this black beard of mine is grown again. So why should I go to so much trouble?"

Before long, Amenda forgot his timidity, and the two were chatting together like old friends. Beethoven hid a kindly, childlike nature under his gruff and uncouth exterior, and the younger man found his admiration of the artist deepening into love for the man himself.

As soon as he had finished dressing, Beethoven pressed a violin into Amenda's hands. Prince Lichnowsky had recently presented him with a fine quartet of stringed instruments,* and Beethoven was extremely proud of them. He and Amenda played together interminably, until at length Beethoven forgot his companion and began to improvise. Amenda set aside his violin and listened breath-

* Preserved in the Beethoven House at Bonn.

lessly. He had heard much of the marvelous power of the master to weave new melodies as he played, and it had been his greatest hope that some day he might hear him.

The gloomy expression which Beethoven usually wore gradually lightened, and he played with an inspiration that seemed superhuman. There were times when Amenda wondered that the clavier could stand such a volume of sound; then in the next moment the music would die down to the faintest whisper.

Finally Beethoven sat silent, with bowed head, before the instrument. Amenda was so deeply moved that he could not speak; at length he whispered, half to himself:

"Ah, what a pity—what an inestimable pity that such glorious music is born and lost in a moment!"

Beethoven looked up in surprise. "You are mistaken—it is not lost." He laid his hand on the clavier. "I can repeat every modulation," he said gravely, and to Amenda's incredulous surprise he once more played in exactly the same manner, recalling every change of melody.

Twilight was falling before Amenda could bring himself to end this rare visit. He felt it was an experience that could never have an equal in his life. As he prepared to leave, Beethoven also reached for his hat.

"I will go with you to your house," he said, placing his hand affectionately on the younger man's shoulder.

When they reached Amenda's lodgings, nothing would

do but he must hear the tone of Carl Friedrich's own violin. It was the signal for more music. Beethoven ended the visit with as much regret as did his companion.

He looked inquiringly at his new friend. "I suppose you can accompany me back?"

Amenda was more than willing. Once again they repaired to Beethoven's rooms and continued their music far into the night.

From that time on the two became inseparable. If friends chanced to see one of them alone on the street they would call out, "Where is the other one?"

"Why have you never written a string quartet?" Amenda asked Beethoven one day.

The latter looked thoughtful. "It takes a real musician to write quartets."

Amenda began to laugh. "Then of course *you* wouldn't attempt it! But aren't you working on your first symphony now?"

"I'm not sure but a symphony is easier to write than a string quartet," his friend insisted.

"Well—what about all those trios?"

Beethoven chuckled. "Speaking of trios, did you hear

what Haydn had to say about the one I finished last month
—the Trio in C minor?" * Amenda shook his head.
"Kozeluch, they tell me, was so disgusted that he threw
the music on the floor and cried, 'We would have done
that differently, wouldn't we, Papa?' "

Amenda laughed. "I suppose Haydn agreed?"

" 'Yes,' he answered; 'we *would* have done that differently.' "

"Haydn doesn't like 'modern' music," laughed Amenda.
"But seriously now, you must write some quartets. Prince
Lobkowitz, I think, would be interested. You know he
plays second violin with his own quartet, and he is always
looking for new music. I'll speak to him about it."

Soon after, Prince Lobkowitz—one of Vienna's wealthiest patrons of music—commissioned Beethoven to write
six quartets. The composer found that this form of music-
writing appealed to him more than any that he had ever
before undertaken. One day while he was working on the
F Major Quartet (Opus 18, No. 1), Amenda came in to
see him. Beethoven, much affected by what he had just
been writing, motioned his friend to a chair.

"Listen to this, Amenda," he said, seating himself before
the clavier. "What does this music suggest to you?"

He began to play a piano version of the F Major's lovely

* Opus 9, No. 3, for violin, viola, and 'cello.

Adagio affetuoso ed appassionata. When he had finished, Amenda—greatly moved—exclaimed, "It is like a picture describing the parting of two lovers!"

Beethoven nodded his head with satisfaction. "I was thinking of Romeo and Juliet as I wrote it—the scene in the burial vault. Do you like it?"

Amenda thought the Adagio one of the most beautiful and profoundly tragic pieces he had ever heard.

When the quartet was finished, Beethoven sent a copy to his friend. On the title page he wrote:

DEAR AMENDA:

Take this quartet as a small memorial of our friendship, and whenever you play it recall the days we passed together and the sincere affection felt for you then and which will always be felt by

Your true and warm friend,
LUDWIG VAN BEETHOVEN

Vienna 1799. June 25th.

On a gloomy afternoon in the fall of 1799, Amenda climbed the endless stairs to Beethoven's lodgings. Within the narrow quarters he found his friend even more melancholy than the weather. Ludwig raised his eyes in deep dejection as Amenda entered the room.

"Money—money!" he grumbled. "What a pity that art has to wait on such vulgar necessities." He sighed mournfully. "Always some new debt of those plagued brothers of mine, and now . . . Now see what a mess I am in!—the landlord demanding his rent, and my last cent gone to Johann only yesterday."

Amenda looked at his friend sympathetically, wishing that he could help him; but he was very nearly as destitute as the composer himself. At that moment they heard the landlord at the door. Beethoven gave Amenda a desperate look.

"Honored sir—" the man began respectfully as he came in, but when he noticed the hopeless look on Beethoven's face he became more coolly insolent. "I can wait no longer for the rent money. Either it must be paid immediately, or—"

Amenda had a flash of inspiration. He interrupted the landlord haughtily: "My good man, no need to make such a fuss!" The landlord looked up with renewed hope: here probably was a wealthy friend who would produce his precious money.

Amenda rubbed his chin thoughtfully. "Suppose you return in, say—well, let us say three hours, and your rent shall be paid."

When the landlord had bowed his way out, Beethoven stared at his friend in surprise. "And where do you expect the money to come from?" he exclaimed.

"That is quite simple if you will only do as I say,"

Amenda answered calmly. He took a paper, wrote down two or three bars of music on it, then hummed over to himself what he had written.

"This will do," he said. *"Freudvoll und Leidvoll* we will call it—joyful and sad. Only it should be *first* sad and *then* joyful to fit the case!"

Beethoven looked at him with a puzzled frown, but Amenda made no explanations. "Here, now," he said, "sit down and do some variations on the theme I have written for you. *Immediately,"* he added, as his friend looked ready to refuse.

"This is a pretty time to write music!" Beethoven began indignantly.

Ignoring the gathering thunder in his friend's eyes, Amenda pushed him into a chair before his writing table, thrust a pencil into his hand, and left him. He shut the door carefully and locked it on the outside.

Three hours later the key grated once more in the lock, and Amenda entered with as much unconcern as if he were paying an ordinary visit.

Beethoven turned on him furiously. "What do you mean by treating me like this?"

Amenda was quite composed. "Have you finished the variations?" he inquired.

Beethoven thrust a piece of paper at him. "There's your stuff!" he said crossly.

Amenda called down jubilantly to the landlord: "Come up at once. Your rent is ready!"

The man puffed up the stairs in glad expectation, but when he saw the paper his expression changed. "What! Do you think me fool enough to accept this in place of real money?"

Amenda laughed indulgently. "Do not be too sure about that! Just take this paper to the music publisher, Herr Mollo, on the Hofstrasse, and see if it is not the best rent you were ever paid!"

The man made off, still dubious. By this time Beethoven's fit of temper had vanished entirely, for he saw at last what Amenda's purpose was. There were tears in his eyes when he turned to him. "Thou priceless one," he said, his voice shaking. "How can I thank thee?" It was typical of the great man's nature that he had often written music before in order to help his friends out, but it had never occurred to him to apply the same remedy to his own case.

In a few moments the landlord returned, hastening up the stairs. His opinion of his lodger had changed considerably since his visit to the publisher. "If the gentleman has any more scraps of paper like that . . . ?" he asked hope-fully.

Amenda escorted him to the door with mock gravity. "Yes, there are many who would like such scraps!"

When he had closed the door on the landlord, Amenda returned thoughtfully to Beethoven's side. "You should travel," he said seriously. "A concert tour, now, would earn you enough to relieve all these little difficulties for a long time."

Beethoven gazed reflectively out of the window. "Yes, I have thought of it."

"Italy," Amenda went on. "That would be the place to go—the land of sapphire seas and golden oranges! Those Southerners have a passion for music, and with your repu-tation . . ."

Beethoven grew enthusiastic. "You are right, my dear fellow. I will go to Italy. But only on condition that you accompany me."

They put their heads together like two schoolboys and sat late into the night planning the wonderful trip. It was to be not only a financial enterprise, but an adventure into the land of romance.

A few days later, however, an unexpected tragedy put an end to their planning. Amenda's brother was killed in an accident, and it became necessary for Beethoven's young friend to return home immediately and take up the duty of caring for the family.

Beethoven could not bear to think of taking the trip without Amenda. "Since you cannot go with me," he wrote, "I shall not go to Italy."

CHAPTER XI

GIULIETTA

(1800)

ONE MOMENT, my good man, *wait!* . . ." Beethoven leaned far out of his window and called to the departing teamster below. Before the driver could collect his wits the musician ran down the stairs and dashed into the street.

"Here! . . ." he said breathlessly. "I will pay you now,

and you can see that the horses have a good feed on the way." He thrust some money into the man's hand. "You understand, now? The market place at the village—I will meet you there."

With a pull at his cap and a chirp to his four horses the man started off. Beethoven watched the precious load go slowly down the street and followed it anxiously with his eyes. His personal belongings—a trunk or two and some scattered clothing—they did not matter. But the piles of music, those children of his brain, and, topping the load, his pianoforte—these were more valuable to him than gold.

Beethoven slowly climbed the long flights of stairs again to gather one or two forgotten things. He whistled happily, though with singular tunelessness, as he stuffed his pockets with bread and cheese and a length of choice salami sausage.

What a day it was! The sun shone brightly and yet was not too hot; the early summer air sparkled with life and energy, and Beethoven was in such haste to be off that he almost forgot his notebook and pencil—those inseparable companions of every ramble.

He had been waiting for weeks now until the weather should settle and he could start for his beloved country. Each spring the city grew intolerable to him; he could not be happy until he was able to shake its dust from his feet and seek out the quiet and peace of the outdoor world.

This summer he was particularly eager for fresh inspiration. It had been eight years now since he first came to Vienna, but although he was recognized as one of the leading musicians of the day, he was not yet satisfied. Music seemed to him too high an art to be always limited by the set rules and regulations that Haydn and Albrechtsberger had tried so hard to hold him to. He instinctively rebelled against sophistication, and he felt that the old classic style of composing should make way for a freer, more romantic interpretation.

This was the year 1800, and Beethoven's thirtieth birthday was not far off. An era of political revolutions had opened. The revolt of peoples against oppressive monarchs was not to reach its peak till the mid-nineteenth century; but it had already begun—with the war by which the Americans won their independence, and with the French Revolution some ten years ago. Was it not fitting, then, that music should also throw aside the limitations of the past and begin a new era?

Beethoven started with a light heart on his walk to the little village in the Austrian Tyrol where he had planned to spend his summer. It was a long distance away, but he did not mind. The longer the better, for then he could have just so much more time to himself, away from the noise of the city and in close communion with Nature. He had a passion for walking. As soon as the fine weather set in, he would spend long days alone in the open country, wandering aimlessly through the fields, stopping now and then to listen to the song of the birds or to jot down some musical inspiration.

Once out of the city his troubles and anxieties were all forgotten. He became as gay as the larks above—as care-free as the daisies nodding at his feet. He had not even told his brothers Carl and Johann where he was going. They were always after him, and he wanted for a time to be rid of their incessant demands.

The outline for a new symphony began to shape itself in his mind. Gradually the world slipped away, and he forgot both time and place.

"Himmel!" Beethoven exclaimed aloud as he noticed the lengthening shadows. "What have I been thinking of to let the hours go by so quickly!"

The sun was close to the western horizon, and the village was still some miles away. He thought with dismay of the cart and its priceless load and wondered if the driver would still be waiting for him. He was hot and tired and hungry—it seemed cruel to have to come back from his beautiful world of illusion to this hard life of weariness and re-sponsibility.

It was dusk before Beethoven finally reached the little village and began to hunt for his possessions. When he came to the market place a sorry spectacle met his eyes.

The cart driver, tired of waiting for him to arrive, had

dumped the contents of his wagon into the middle of the square. Beethoven's treasured pianoforte rested in the mud; his trunks were strewn about the ground and piled haphazard on top of books and extra clothing. But when the master discovered his music scattered to the winds and blowing in all directions, that was the last straw.

"*Donnerwetter!* Somebody shall pay for this!" he cried furiously, running about in a wild effort to recover the precious sheets. The villagers gathered in groups and watched him from a safe distance. He was about to turn on them in his fury when a sound close by penetrated his angry consciousness.

A low peal of laughter, soft and melodious, floated down apparently from the sky. Probably to one less musically attuned the sound might have passed unnoticed, but to the weary Beethoven it was like a soothing touch upon his brow. He looked eagerly around.

Close to the market place an old inn raised its ivy-covered walls, and from a window under the eaves a young girl watched the scene below. It was growing too dark to make out her features very plainly, but Beethoven could see that she was young and attractive. A few dark curls escaped from beneath her cap of snowy muslin, and even in the dying light he could distinguish the dimples playing about her laughing lips. No doubt it was some village maiden entertained by his plight.

The musician's spirits rose. He was always susceptible to feminine charm, but lately all his time had been spent among people of the nobility and upper circles of Vienna, where a person of low birth, no matter how great his reputation, was not considered the equal of young ladies of the aristocracy. It would be a relief to meet a maid on her own grounds—especially if she were blessed with beauty!

Beethoven suddenly realized how comical his whole plight must appear. His anger vanished, and with a roar of laughter he enlisted the help of the amused villagers to repair the havoc which the cart driver had left.

It was nearly twelve o'clock before he finally got his things all gathered together and safely stowed away in a room at the inn. He threw himself wearily into bed, tired, yet with keen anticipation of what the next day might bring.

Beethoven hardly slept for fear of missing his first dawn in the country. He kept waking up and watching the gray square of light that was his window. As soon as it began to pale, he was up and eager to be out.

First, though, his bath. He had a passion for water, and

since tubs were an almost unknown luxury in those days, he would stand in his wash basin and pour the cold liquid over his body in large pitcherfuls. What matter if most of it went on the floor?

Soon he was out in the open, drawing in great breaths of the sweet morning air and striding up the hillside by a little path that wound through the forest. He felt as if he had been released from prison after the long winter months in the city. Here at last he could work! Out came the little notebook, and as he walked he stopped frequently to jot down some musical phrase.

The narrow path he was following continued to wind and finally started back down the hill toward the village. As he turned a sharp corner Beethoven came suddenly upon an enchanting vision. Seated on a rock at the edge of the path, a young girl, fresher than the morning itself, sat looking down at the little town beneath. Her cheeks were as pink as the wild roses at her feet, with dimples hiding in their soft curves, and her eyes matched the chestnut of her curls. Her lips seemed made for laughter, and when she found herself discovered by a much startled stranger, the same low peal he had heard the evening before greeted Beethoven.

"Forgive me, Fräulein," he began in confusion.

The girl slid demurely from the rock and dropped him

a curtsy. "Pray do not mention it, sir!" Her voice was as musical as her laughter, and she looked up at him mischievously. "Did you thoroughly punish that dreadful cart driver for abandoning your possessions?"

Beethoven smiled ruefully; it was gratifying to know that she had recognized him, but he feared she must have received a very unfortunate impression of him the evening before. "It was only your sense of humor that saved the entire village from destruction!" he said gallantly. She laughed again, and Beethoven thought he had never heard such a charming sound.

He told her of his absent-mindedness and what trouble it caused him. "Once," he said, "Prince Lichnowsky insisted that I ride his horse. I couldn't do that—" he looked at the girl, hoping she would understand his love of independence—"so I bought a horse of my own." He began to laugh. "But after I had bought the horse I promptly forgot his existence until several months later, when the rascally stable keeper presented me with an enormous bill for his food! That was the end of *my* experience with horses."

The girl nodded sympathetically. She seemed so interested that he found himself telling her all manner of things that he had never confided to anyone before. He was highly gratified to see the impression which he, a perfect stranger, was able to make on this beautiful girl. It did not occur to him that she might know his identity and was flattered at his attention because she had heard that he was a great musician.

In his usual way when deeply engrossed, Beethoven grew oblivious of his surroundings and failed to notice the approach of a third person. But the girl saw the elegantly gowned, gray-haired woman who toiled up the path with fretful effort. She ran to meet her.

"Giulietta, naughty child!" the lady cried. "I have been hunting everywhere for you. What do you mean by wandering off alone like this so early in the morning?"

Giulietta put her arms around the older woman.

"Now, Mother dearest, don't scold," she said coaxingly. "Surely it's all right to have a little freedom here in the country, so far from the strict rules of the city!"

Her mother still looked disapproving and glanced with suspicion at the stranger. But Giulietta turned with enthusiasm toward her new friend.

"This is the great Herr van Beethoven!" She curtsied again with exaggerated formality. "My mother, sir, the Countess Guicciardi."

"This way—" Beethoven said gently—"the fingers a little higher!" He held Giulietta's white fingers carefully in the right position and noted with a sigh what a contrast they were to his own stumpy hands, covered with black hair.

For several weeks now he had been teaching her daily, and his admiration for the beautiful girl was constantly increasing. She, on her side, flattered by the attention that the great musician paid her small efforts, showed him more kindness than he had dared to hope for. Giulietta and her mother had expected to be thoroughly bored at this quiet watering place in the country, and Beethoven's music was a welcome diversion.

Like all young ladies of the aristocracy, Giulietta had played the pianoforte since she was a child. She had even mastered some of Beethoven's sonatas, which were very fashionable at that time. He had already written about a dozen, and they were considered extremely difficult.

"But I'll never be able to play them as well as young Carl Czerny does," she said, sighing. "Have you heard that boy? No? He really is amazing. I shall have to send him to you when you return to Vienna. He is not yet ten, but he plays like an angel."

"Ah, Fräulein Giulietta," Beethoven began tenderly, bending towards the girl, *"you* are like an angel . . ."

"Giulietta!" a dry voice interrupted, as the Countess

Guicciardi entered the room, "it is time we made arrangements to pay for your lessons."

Beethoven sprang up in deep offense. "Don't mention such a thing!" he said, his eyes flashing. "I cannot hear of it!" He turned precipitately and left the room.

Giulietta looked after him in dismay, but the Countess shook her head disdainfully.

"He is too proud," she said, "and he has nothing to be proud about. The other day I asked him if the 'van' in his name stood for nobility, as 'von' does in our part of the country. And what do you suppose he answered?" Giulietta shook her head slightly. "He drew himself up with all the pride of a prince and pointed to his head and to his heart. 'Madame,' he said arrogantly, 'my nobility lies here—and here!'" The Countess smiled with a superior expression. "The innkeeper tells me that Van Beethoven is a Flemish name and means a 'garden of beets'—not much nobility in that!"

"Ah, well, Mother," Giulietta replied lightly, "perhaps Herr van Beethoven is right. He has a noble heart in spite of his rough manners, and surely he must have noble thoughts to write such wonderful music!" She knit her pretty forehead. "But we must do *something* in return for all these lessons he has been giving me. I know! I shall sew him a fine linen shirt; those he has are in a sad condition."

When, a few days later, Giulietta presented the new shirt to Beethoven half afraid that he might refuse it as violently as her mother's offer, he received it with emotion and deep gratitude.

"You made it yourself for me?" he exclaimed, clasping the gift to his heart. "Ah, Fräulein, I shall treasure it as long as I live!" He held out a freshly written sheet of music. "I have composed a new rondo for you—but it is a small return for so fine a gift as yours."

Giulietta flushed with pleasure. This was what she had been playing for, with her arch glances and winning smiles—though she was disappointed that it was not a sonata.

Some time later, however, Beethoven asked her to return the music. "I must send a little gift to the Countess Henriette, the wife of Prince Lichnowsky's brother. I wonder—" he hesitated a little—"would you let me have the Rondo back?"

The girl bit her lip in vexation, but before she could answer, Beethoven continued, "I'll give you a sonata in exchange. It is dedicated to you."

This was the lovely *Sonata quasi una fantasia,* whose serene, gently flowing first movement has reminded many listeners of moonlight playing over quiet waters.*

---

* Not until some time later, however, did Opus 27, No. 2, become known as the "Moonlight Sonata." Although it has ever since been called by this popular name, it was not Beethoven himself who so christened it.

Sonata quasi una fantasia, Opus 27, No. 2 ("Moonlight"),
second movement

During the weeks that followed, Beethoven's infatuation for the lovely Giulietta continued to grow stronger. There were times when he thought that she returned his love—so kind she seemed. Then again she was cool and distant, and he lost all hope.

He longed to tell her of his feelings, but he was far from eloquent, and in her presence he never seemed able to express himself in words. Music was the real language of his heart; perhaps through its means he would be able to make her realize his love. And, if she cared for him, she could not fail to understand—and to answer by some token.

"I should like to play for you, Fräulein Giulietta," he said to her one evening shortly before the Guicciardis were to return to Vienna.

In those days Beethoven was more celebrated as a performer than as a composer. Giulietta and her mother needed no second invitation; they settled themselves with a little flutter of anticipation as the composer went over to the piano.

Through the open window came the light of a full moon. The late summer air was heavy with the perfume of jasmine, and in the distance a cricket chirped lazily. Beethoven looked at Giulietta with emotion; then he blew out the candle that stood on the piano. The moon's dim light filled the room with a mysterious radiance.

First the music came softly, floating on the air like a caress; then it grew bolder and more passionate, until it spoke in mighty terms of the majesty that love brings to noble hearts. As Beethoven played, an invisible presence seemed to hover over him, the spirit of music incarnate.

Giulietta was strangely stirred. This ugly man, so careless of the smaller things of life, so deeply centered in the highest, moved in a world apart from hers. She felt that she could never reach such heights. . . .

When he had finished, Beethoven sat silent a moment, his head bowed before the piano. All of Giulietta's pretty little phrases faded away, and with a feeling very close to reverence she and her mother left the room quietly. As she went out the girl cast a glance of tenderness and pity at the young musician. But he looked up in time only to catch the cynical smile of the Countess as she closed the door.

He felt suddenly very lonely and very tired. And there was a peculiar ringing in his ears. For some time now he had noticed it occasionally, but tonight it was much stronger. It frightened him.

Beethoven sat for a long time staring at the keyboard before him. As the rays of the moon slowly spread through the room, so a new understanding flooded his soul. He was no longer lonely and sad. The music he had played for Giulietta echoed in his heart and comforted him. He saw that in spite of disappointments and hardships life held for him a rare compensation—the power of creation.

He lifted his head proudly and looked out into the stillness of the night. The presence that his music had evoked seemed to be saying: "My chosen ones must pay a price exceeding high. Loneliness and misfortune shall be their lot—but also joy and exaltation beyond the ordinary comprehension of man."

CHAPTER XII

TWO FAMOUS PUPILS

(1 8 0 1)

"Forty-five . . . fifty . . . fifty-one . . . *Donner-wetter!*" Beethoven cried in exasperation. "How can anyone make a decent cup of coffee with only fifty-one coffee beans?"

He shivered and drew the dressing-gown closer about his shoulders. It was always cold in these lodgings in the Tiefen Graben, and he had been hard at work since dawn with his composing. Every morning he arose at the first sign of light and began writing. By nine o'clock he was more than ready for his coffee and rolls.

But he was most particular about the coffee. He had instructed his servant to count out sixty beans—no more, no less—and lay them carefully in a bowl next to his coffee machine. This was the second time that she had failed in the number.

He reached violently for the bell. Decidedly this slattern would have to go, he thought dismally, remembering how many others he had already discharged.

A slovenly servant answered his call.

"What does this mean?" Beethoven began angrily. "Is it impossible, then, for you to count?" Suddenly, in the midst of his scolding, there was a knock at the door.

The woman shuffled over to see who was there, while Beethoven relieved his feelings by kicking a stray boot into the center of the room. At best, his apartment was far from orderly, but this morning it presented a sadder appearance than usual. His nightclothes, forgotten in the pressure of an early inspiration, lay in the middle of the floor. Other articles of clothing were strewn about, and the remains of a late supper decorated the chairs. Everywhere lay sheets of music, piles of manuscript, and books covered with dust.

A slight, nervous man, accompanied by a small boy of perhaps ten or eleven years of age, was ushered into the room. They were strangers to Beethoven, and he scowled at the unwelcome interruption.

"Sir," the man said, "I hope you will forgive this early visit. We were told that you are usually away from home later in the day." He pushed the boy forward. "The Countess Giulietta Guicciardi said you might be good enough to hear my son."

Beethoven's eyes lit up at the mention of Giulietta's name. She was betrothed now to the Count von Gallenberg, but he would never forget his love for her. He turned with interest to the boy.

"Allow me, sir," the man went on, "to present my son, Carl Czerny."

Beethoven drew the child to him and looked at him. "I remember hearing about you, my lad," he said kindly. "The Countess spoke to me often of your playing. Will you let me listen to you?"

The boy, who had spent months in preparing for this moment, nodded eagerly. Beethoven had been his god ever since the child first began to play the clavier. Now that he actually stood face to face with the master, each detail of the great man's appearance engraved itself indelibly on Carl's mind. Beethoven was wearing a shaggy morning suit of wool, and with the thick stubble of his unshaven beard he made the boy think of his favorite character, Robinson Crusoe. Childlike, he did not fail to notice the cotton steeped in yellow ointment that filled the composer's ears, though he little suspected the tragedy that was creeping over the master.

With trembling fingers young Czerny began to play Mozart's C Major Piano Concerto. Beethoven was astonished at the brilliance and power of the boy's playing. He sat down beside him and filled in the orchestral parts with his left hand.

"Not so bad, child!" he exclaimed warmly when Carl had finished.

Encouraged, the boy plunged into one of the master's own compositions. When he had finished, Beethoven turned to the father. "Your son has marked ability," he said. "I will teach him myself if you will bring him to me several times a week."

Czerny could hardly believe his ears. He had heard that it was almost impossible to persuade the master to accept new pupils.

Beethoven stroked the boy's hair and seemed loath to let him go. He turned impulsively to the father. "Will you leave him with me for the day?" he asked. Carl held his breath for fear his father might refuse. But the elder Czerny was highly flattered at the master's interest.

"Until this evening, then," said Beethoven, escorting the man to the door.

Carl hugged himself silently in joyful anticipation.

The day that followed stood out forever in the child's memory. First he was made to share in the coffee and rolls of the belated breakfast. Then Beethoven gave him a lesson on the piano, and it was a revelation to the boy to see how patiently the master attended to every detail and made him go over and over the difficult passages. He could excuse a few wrong notes, he said, but when it came to the *expression* of the music he was particularly strict.

"Anyone can overlook a false note or two occasionally," Beethoven explained. "I make mistakes myself sometimes," he went on with a laugh; "but an error of expression—that is inexcusable; it shows a lack of attention, knowledge, or, even worse, of feeling!"

Young Czerny attended every word carefully. In his eagerness to learn he was like the dry earth drinking up precious raindrops.

Presently Beethoven's attention wandered, and he rose from his seat beside the boy. He hurried to his writing table and began to search absent-mindedly. Carl noticed the confusion that reigned everywhere and wondered if the master could ever find what he was after. Papers of all kinds lay scattered over the desk. A quantity of small figures and statuettes, bells of every size and description, and finally an overturned inkstand added to the hopeless disorder.

Beethoven searched vainly for a few moments. "It is too aggravating!" he exclaimed with irritation. "Everything is done to vex me!" He looked helplessly around him. "I am really the most orderly of creatures," he said, half in anger and half defiantly. "That old witch of a servant must have hidden my manuscript," he grumbled under his breath.

Finally he gave up in despair. "It is no use hunting. Very likely the woman has used the sheets to wipe my boots with. It would not be the first time!" he added darkly.

Carl watched with astonishment as Beethoven went to the window and, pulling wider one of the wooden shutters, began to write some musical phrases on the smooth wood. The boy noticed that the shutters were almost filled with similar notes, and he wondered what the master would do when there was no further space. But just at that moment Beethoven discovered the corner of a manuscript sticking out from beneath a pile of books on the floor.

Still oblivious of Carl's presence, he pounced on the paper, drew it quickly from its hiding place, and began to work at it feverishly. Young Czerny sat patiently at the piano, almost afraid to breathe for fear of disturbing the great man. But he needn't have worried—the master was not even conscious of his existence.

After a half-hour of uninterrupted writing, Beethoven began to show signs of restlessness. He ran his fingers through his shaggy hair and made it stand up in an even more disorderly fashion than before. At length he left his desk and, with a look of abstraction, picked up a pitcher of water and began to pour it over his head. The child gasped in dismay as the liquid spilled over the floor in floods, while Beethoven, his mind engrossed in an obstinate musical phrase, paid no attention to what was happening.

All at once an angry voice was heard on the stairs, and the landlord appeared at the door.

"Decidedly, this is too much!" he exclaimed with indignation. "Are we to be constantly deluged with water coming through the ceiling besides having to put up with the infernal racket that goes on here continually?"

Beethoven looked at him in mild surprise, scarcely roused from his preoccupation.

"Herr van Beethoven, you will kindly find another lodging place," the angry man went on. "We cannot stand this any longer." Without another word he banged the door and stamped down the stairs.

A savage scowl began to deepen on Beethoven's face. Then his glance fell on Carl, who sat at the piano without daring to speak or move. He shrugged his shoulders with a laugh.

"It makes no difference. I'm always changing my lodgings." He looked around the shabby room. "This place is much too cold; the last one didn't have enough sun, and the time before it was the landlord who annoyed me with his obsequious bowing and scraping. And before that—well, now, I've forgotten just what was the matter then." He broke off with a shout of laughter, completely restored to good humor.

"Shall we go on with our lesson?" he cried.

Soon after, the slovenly servant came in to say that dinner was ready. Shuffling about in heelless slippers, she drew out a table from the corner, and behold, another trans-formation of Beethoven's narrow apartment! It had been successively dressing-room, living-room, and music-room, and it now became a dining-room.

The boy's eyes took in every detail of the scene. There was only one picture on the wall—a portrait in oil of an elderly gentleman wearing a tasseled cap and holding a roll of music in one hand.

Beethoven saw the child's interest and looked up at the picture of old Ludwig. "That was my grandfather," he said simply, yet with a touch of emotion in his voice. "A wonderful character! I was only three when he died, but I remember him as distinctly as if it were yesterday that we wandered through the fields together. That portrait has been with me for close to thirty years—a fortune would not tempt me to part with it!"

The servant laid a spotted cloth and cracked china on the table. To young Czerny they seemed like shining porcelain and snowy damask; for his ardent young imagination made everything connected with the master appear hallowed by the association.

Beethoven had forgotten his anger over the landlord. One of the most extraordinary things about him was the sudden change forever active in his temper. He would plunge from the highest good humor to the most violent anger, and before the astonished spectator had time to collect his wits, he was back once more to good nature.

"What luck!" he cried as they sat down at the table. "This is Friday. I hope you are as fond of fish as I am?" He looked anxiously at the child. Carl nodded violently; he would have been fond of sawdust if the master had expressed a preference for it. "All good Catholics have fish on Friday," Beethoven went on, "but," he winked jovially, "I have it because it's my favorite dish, especially when accompanied by a good large platter of macaroni!" He looked hopefully toward the kitchen.

Just then the servant appeared with a tray bearing a covered tureen and a bowl of eggs.

She set them down in front of Beethoven; he lifted the lid from the tureen and looked with appreciation at the thick bread soup it contained. Solemnly he broke an egg and sniffed its contents before adding it to the soup. Another egg was opened and another; but the last one unfortunately proved stale. Beethoven raised an angry glance.

"What do you mean by bringing me stale eggs?" he said indignantly, looking down at the offending object in his hand. Then suddenly, without further warning, he threw it violently at the servant. The egg caught her full on the head, and dripped into her hair and eyes in an ill-smelling mass. She burst into tears and fled to the kitchen.

Beethoven looked after her ruefully. "There! Now I've done it," he said, forgetting his anger. "Poor girl—I didn't mean to hurt her, but—" he frowned—"she should be more careful with her eggs!" He sat a moment staring at the broken eggshells, then put his hand into his pocket and drew out a shining coin. "Perhaps I had better apologize!" He winked at Carl as he went into the kitchen.

As soon as dinner was finished, Beethoven reached for his hat. Rain or shine, snow or hail, he always spent the afternoon hours out of doors. The weather never seemed to affect him; he loved Nature under all conditions, and it was on these long rambles through the country that musical ideas came to him most readily. He went into the open as a bee goes out for honey, and never failed to come back richly laden.

"You don't mind a little walk?" he asked young Czerny. Carl looked up with enthusiasm. To be seen on the streets of Vienna with the great man—what an honor!

Beethoven stuffed his precious notebook into his pocket. He noticed how intently the boy watched him, and pulled the book out to show him.

"Like Joan of Arc," he said with a laugh, "I never go without my banner." He turned some of the pages of the little book and showed Carl the closely written notes and painstaking corrections he had made.

"Remember, child," he said solemnly, "if you should ever write music, careful work is what counts! No matter how good the idea may be, it needs working over—must be rewritten many times."

In later years this advice stood the boy in good stead. When he began to compose he was so conscientious in his work, so careful in its revision, that his famous books of exercises still remain the standard of technique.

Beethoven turned his steps toward the open country. They walked until the child felt he would drop from weariness, yet he would not for worlds have admitted that he was tired. After a few attempts at conversation Carl was silent. Beethoven did not seem to notice him. Either he was too much engrossed in his own thoughts, or else he did not hear him. . . .

When they returned to his lodgings, Beethoven went immediately to the piano and began to improvise. There was a haunting sadness in the music, but Carl noticed that as the master played, the sorrow left his face, and he seemed comforted—as if he had found refuge in a happier environment.

Near the writing table young Czerny saw two framed mottoes:

I AM THAT WHICH IS. I AM ALL THAT
IS, THAT WAS, THAT WILL BE.
NO MORTAL MAN HAS EVER LIFTED
MY VEIL.

HE IS ALONE AND SOLELY OF HIMSELF,
AND TO THIS ONLY ONE ALL THINGS
OWE THEIR EXISTENCE.

To the boy's childish mind the words were meaningless, but he sensed their deep religious nature and understood vaguely that here was a man who had no sympathy with the narrow forms of accepted religion, yet believed implicitly in God.

Beethoven was still lost in his music when the elder

Czerny returned for his son. Without disturbing him, they quietly withdrew.

Carl never forgot the picture of that moment—Beethoven with his shaggy head bent over the keyboard—the shadows of the early winter twilight softening the disorder of the room, and finally the melancholy grandeur of the master's music.

A few weeks later, Beethoven was just about to leave for his daily walk when a young boy knocked at his door.

"May I speak with you a moment, sir?"

Beethoven hesitated a moment. He was about to say, "Come back some other time," when something in the tall, lanky youth's appearance made him stop. The boy was about seventeen, and wore shabby clothes of a country cut. Beethoven was reminded of his own first trip to Vienna, when he too, a boy of seventeen, had sought out the great Mozart.

"My father said that he would write to you about me," the youth continued, twisting his rough felt hat in his hands.

A smile broke over the composer's gloomy features. "Are you by any chance the son of Franz Ries?" His visitor nodded eagerly.

Beethoven stretched out both hands. "You are welcome,

my boy!" he exclaimed cordially. "I haven't time to write to your father now, but tell him that I have not forgotten how my mother died. With that he will be satisfied." It was not until later that Ferdinand Ries learned of the assistance that his father had given the musician's family at the time of Maria-Magdalena's death.

Beethoven pressed the boy for news from home. He was eager to hear about all his old neighbors and friends.

"Do you recall Herr Pfeiffer?" Ries inquired.

Beethoven threw up his hands. "Tobias Pfeiffer! How could I ever forget the man who was the first—after my father—to teach me music!"

The boy shook his head. "Ah, it is sad. He was once a great musician, they say, and now he is sick and poor with no one to care for him!"

Beethoven sighed with real feeling. "Poor fellow! Perhaps I can do something to help him. I will send some money this very day." Just then he noticed the threadbare appearance of the boy's own clothes and questioned him about his circumstances.

Ferdinand admitted that he was practically penniless.

"I went first to Munich," he told the master, "but it was impossible to get along there. The only work I could find was the copying of some music at fifty pfennigs a sheet." He smiled ruefully. "When I had saved seven ducats I started for Vienna."

Beethoven clapped him on the shoulder. "Seven ducats to reach Vienna!" he laughed. "You must have walked a good part of the distance!" He put his hand in his pocket. "Here," he said kindly, pressing a coin into Ferdinand's hand, "go and find a place to eat and sleep, and tomorrow you shall come to me for a lesson."

He would not listen to the boy's remonstrances and thanks, but pushed him gently out of the door. Little did he suspect that Ferdinand Ries was to become one of his most famous pupils. He only thought that here was an opportunity to repay the boy's father for his generosity of former years.

Beethoven took a great fancy to young Ferdinand Ries. He gave him lessons daily and was amazed at the extraordinary ease with which the boy could write music. It was not long before he let him help in the copying of his own manuscripts.

Ries often accompanied the composer on his long walks through the country. One day the boy heard a shepherd in the distance, playing a flute. It was a sad, singularly sweet melody, and Ferdinand listened in delight. He looked up to see what the master thought of it, but Beethoven seemed oblivious. The youth touched his arm.

"Isn't it lovely?" he asked.

Beethoven turned with a start. "What's that?"

"The shepherd's flute—off there in the distance."

The master looked at him queerly. "I don't hear any flute. What flute?" he asked.

Ries pointed to the hills. "Over there," he said. "Isn't it beautifully clear on the cold air?"

Beethoven listened attentively, a worried expression on his face. "You are sure you don't imagine it?"

The boy began to laugh. Surely the master must be joking.

Beethoven said no more, and the two turned homeward. Occasionally he asked, "Do you still hear it—the flute?" and not until Ferdinand finally answered in the negative did the strained expression leave his face.

The master was very quiet on the homeward walk. His eyes were filled with a sorrow which young Ries could not fail to notice, but was unable to understand.

CHAPTER XIII

THE APPROACHING TRAGEDY

(1 8 0 2 - 1 8 0 3)

EARLY IN 1798 Beethoven began to notice an occasional ringing in his ears. Then one evening, as he and Stephan von Breuning were talking together, he suddenly discovered that he could hardly hear his friend's voice. A terrible thought came over him: Could it be possible that he was growing deaf?

After Stephan left, Beethoven threw himself into a chair and buried his face in his hands. The worst tragedy that could befall a musician would be to lose his sense of hearing. Surely fate could not be so cruel!

For a long time he sat there, sunk in despair. Then he went to the piano. Whenever Beethoven was in trouble, or at any time of great emotion, he always turned to music. When he sat at the piano improvising, or at his desk working over some new composition, he was able to forget himself in something greater than his own limited concerns. His personal emotion became the key that unlocked the doors of creative power, and made of him a channel through which healing and inspiration flowed.

Beethoven himself realized this. Once when a friend (the Baroness Ertmann) lost her son, he invited her to

Sonata Pathétique, Opus 13, first movement

visit him. "Now we will talk to each other in music," he said, sitting down at the piano. In telling of the incident the Baroness said: "He played for over an hour—he told me everything and at last brought me comfort."

When another dear friend spent long months on a

sickbed, Beethoven would come into the adjoining room, quietly sit down at the piano, and improvise for an hour or longer. Then he would leave as silently as he had come—content in the knowledge that he had brought comfort to his sick friend.

From those early days when deafness first threatened Beethoven, came some of the most poignant expressions of suffering ever translated into music—the *Sonata Pathétique* in C minor (Opus 13), the opening movement of the Piano Sonata in D (Opus 10, No. 3), and the Adagio from the first String Quartet (Opus 18, No. 1).

Beethoven could not bring himself to speak of his affliction to those around him. He was like a child—a hurt, perplexed child who is too proud to let others know that he suffers, yet longs to confide in someone. There were only two people in the world with whom he was willing to share his secret—Wegeler and Amenda.

He wrote long letters to both of them, describing his condition in detail.

My Good, Dear Wegeler!

How greatly do I thank you for thinking of me; I have so little deserved it and so little tried to deserve anything from you, and yet you are so very good and refuse to be held aloof by anything, not even by my unpardonable remissness, remaining always my true, good brave friend. Do not believe that I could forget you who were always so dear to me. . . .

You want to know something about my situation. It is not so bad. Since last year, unbelievable though it may sound even after I tell you, Lichnowsky, who has always remained my warmest friend (there were little quarrels between us, but they only served to strengthen our friendship), set aside a fixed sum of 600 florins for me to draw against so long as I remained without a position worthy of me.

From my compositions I have a large income and I may say that I have more commissions than it is possible for me to fill. Besides, I have six or seven publishers and might have more if I chose; they no longer bargain with me—I ask, and they pay. You see it is very convenient. For instance, I see a friend in need and my purse does not permit me to help him at once. I have only to sit down and in a short time help is at hand. Moreover, I am a better businessman than formerly. . . .

The only pity is that my evil demon, my bad health, is continually putting a spoke in my wheel, by which I mean that my hearing has grown steadily worse for three years. . . . Frank wanted to tone up my body by tonic medicines and restore my hearing with almond oil, but, *prosit*, nothing came of the effort; my hearing grew worse and worse. . . .

I was really miserable during this winter; I had frightful attacks of colic and I fell back into my previous condition, and so things remained until about four weeks ago, when I went to Vering. . . . He prescribed the lukewarm Danube bath, into which I had each time to pour a little bottle of strengthening stuff, gave me no medicine of any kind until about four weeks ago, when he prescribed pills for my stomach and a kind of tea for my ear. Since then I can say I am stronger and better; only my ears whistle and buzz continually, day and night.

I am living a wretched life; for two years I have avoided almost all social gatherings because it is impossible for me to say to people: "I am deaf." If I belonged to any other profession it would be easier, but in my profession it is an awful state, the more since my enemies, who are not a few, what would they say?

In order to give you an idea of this singular deafness of mine I must tell you that in the theater I must get very close to the orchestra in order to understand the actors. If I am a little distant I do not hear the high tones of the instrument and singers, and if I be but a little farther away I do not hear at all. Frequently I can hear the tones of a low conversation, but not the words, and as soon as anybody shouts, it is intolerable. It seems singular that in conversation there are people who do not notice my condition at all, attributing it to my absent-mindedness.

Heaven knows what will happen to me. *Vering says that there will be an improvement if no complete cure.* I have often cursed my existence; *Plutarch* taught me resignation. If possible I will bid defiance to my fate, although there will be moments in my life when I shall be the unhappiest of God's creatures. I beg of you to say nothing of my condition to anybody, not even to Lorchen. . . . Resignation! What a wretched refuge—and yet the only one open to me.

Forgive me that I add these cares of friendship to yours, which is sorrowful enough as it is. Stephan von Breuning is here now and we are together almost daily; it does me so much good to revive the old emotions. He is really become a good, splendid youngster, who knows a thing or two, and like us all has his heart in the right place. I have a pretty domicile on the bastion which is doubly valuable because of my health. I believe I shall make it possible for Stephan to come and live with me. . . .

I have never forgotten one of you good people even if I did not write to you; but you know that writing was never my forte; the best of my friends have not had a letter from me in years. I live only in my notes and when one composition is scarcely ended, another is already begun. As I compose at present I frequently work on three or four compositions at the same time.

Write to me often, hereafter. I will try occasionally to find time to write to you. Give greetings to all, including the good Madame Councilor, and tell her that I still occasionally have a "raptus.". . .

A word about Ries, whom I greet heartily; so far as his son is concerned I shall write you more in detail, although I think that he would be more fortunate in Paris than in Vienna. Vienna is overcrowded and the most meritorious find it extremely difficult to maintain themselves. In the autumn or winter I shall see what I can do for him, for at that time the public hurries back to the city.

Farewell, good, faithful Wegeler! Be assured of the love and friendship of

Your

BEETHOVEN

MY DEAR, GOOD AMENDA, my cordial friend, I received and read your last letter with mixed pain and pleasure. To what shall I compare your fidelity, your attachment to me? Oh, it is so beautiful that you have always been true to me and I know how to single you out and keep you above all others. You are not a Viennese friend, no, you are one of those who spring from the ground of my native land. How often do I wish you were with me, for your Beethoven is living an unhappy life, quarreling with Nature and its creator. . . . Know that my noblest faculty, my hearing, has greatly deteriorated. When you were still with me I felt the symptoms but kept silent; now it is continually growing worse, and whether or not a cure is possible has become a question. . . .

Oh, how happy would I be if my hearing were completely restored; then would I hurry to you, but as it is I must refrain from everything, and the most beautiful years of my life must pass without accomplishing the promise of my talent and powers. A sad resignation to which I must resort although, indeed, I am resolved to rise superior to every obstacle. But how will that be possible? Yes, Amenda, if my infirmity shows itself to be incurable in half a year, I shall appeal to you; you must abandon everything and come to me.

You will not deny me; you will help your friend bear his cares and affliction. . . . I beg of you to keep the matter of my deafness a profound secret to *be confided to nobody no matter* who it is. Write to me very often. Your letters, no matter how short, comfort me, do me good, and I shall soon expect another from you, my dear fellow.

Now, farewell, my dear, good fellow; if you think I can do something for you here, command me as a matter of course.

Your faithful, and truly affectionate

L. v. BEETHOVEN

In spite of everything, Beethoven's hearing continued to grow worse. It became more and more difficult for him to understand what was said to him, and he began to distrust all his friends. Even Stephan von Breuning was not exempt from his suspicion; after a series of misunderstandings Beethoven quarreled violently with this friend.

Stephan wrote to his brother-in-law and complained with sorrow of the change in Beethoven.

You cannot conceive, my dear Wegeler [he said], what an indescribable, I might say fearful, effect the gradual loss of hearing has had upon him. Think of the feeling of being unhappy in one of such violent temperament; in addition, reserve, mistrust, often towards his best friends, and in many things want of decision! For the greater part, with only an occasional exception, when he gives free vent to his feelings on the spur of the moment, intercourse with him is a real exertion, at which one can scarcely trust to oneself. From May until the beginning of this month we lived in the same house, and at the outset I took him into my rooms. He had scarcely come before he became severely, almost dangerously, ill, and this was followed by an intermittent fever. Worry and the care of him used me rather severely.

Beethoven gradually cut himself off from all his friends. He grew so depressed that his new physician, Professor Schmidt, became much concerned about him.

"You must get away from Vienna," the doctor told him,

"the salutary air and quiet of the country will improve your condition. I should advise you to go to Heiligenstadt for the summer months."

Beethoven was too sunk in misery to care where he went. Even the prospect of getting into the country, where he usually found so much happiness, held no interest for him now.

Beethoven remained in Heiligenstadt for six months, but his condition did not improve. Finally he became convinced that he could not live much longer. As the chill of autumn succeeded the summer months he felt that his days were numbered, and one dismal morning in early October he decided to write his will, ever since then called "the Heiligenstadt Testament."

For my brothers Carl and —— Beethoven. [He could not bring himself to write Johann's name.]

O ye men who think or say that I am malevolent, stubborn or misanthropic, how greatly do ye wrong me, you do not know the secret causes of my seeming. From childhood, my heart and mind were disposed to the gentle feeling of good will, I was ever eager to accomplish great deeds, but reflect now that for six years I have been in a hopeless case, aggravated by senseless physicians, cheated year after year in the hope of improvement, finally compelled to face the prospect of a *lasting malady* (whose cure will take years or, perhaps, be impossible). Born with an ardent and lively temperament, even susceptible to the diversions of society, I was compelled early to isolate myself, to live in loneliness, when I, at times, tried to forget all this, oh, how harshly was I repulsed by the doubly sad experience of my bad hearing, and yet it was impossible for me to say to men speak louder, shout, for I am deaf. Ah how could I possibly admit an infirmity in the *one sense* which should have been more perfect in me than in others, a sense which I once possessed in highest perfection, a perfection such as few surely in my profession enjoy or have ever enjoyed. I cannot do it, therefore forgive me when you see me draw back when I would gladly be with you. . . . If I approach near to people a hot terror seizes me, a fear that I may be subjected to the danger of letting my condition be observed. Thus it has been during the last half year which I spent in the country, commanded by my intelligent physician to spare my hearing as much as possible. . . . I have been brought to the verge of despair; but little more and I would have put an end to my life. Only art it was that withheld me, ah it seemed impossible to leave the world until I had produced all that I felt called upon to produce. And so I endured this wretched existence. . . .

Divine One, thou lookest into my inmost soul, thou knowest it, thou knowest that love of man and desire to do good live therein. O men, when some day you read these words, reflect that ye did me wrong and let the unfortunate one comfort himself and find one of his kind who, despite all the obstacles of nature, yet did all that was in his power to be accepted among worthy artists and men.

You, my brothers Carl and ———, as soon as I am dead, if Dr. Schmidt is still alive, ask him in my name to describe my malady and attach this document to the history of my illness so that so far as is possible at least the world may become reconciled with me after my death. At the same time I declare you to be the heirs of my small fortune (if so it can be called), divide it fairly, bear with and help one another; what injury you have done me, you know was long ago forgiven.

To you, brother Carl, I give special thanks for the attachment you have displayed towards me of late. It is my wish that your lives may be better and freer from care than I have had. Recommend *virtue* to your children, it alone can give happiness, not money. I speak from experience; it was virtue that upheld me in misery; to it next to my art I owe the fact that I did not end my life by suicide.

Farewell and love each other. I thank all my friends, particularly *Prince Lichnowsky* and *Professor Schmidt*. I desire that the instruments from Prince L. be preserved by one of you, but let no quarrel result from this. So soon as they can serve your purpose, sell them—how glad will I be if I can still be helpful to you in my grave. With joy I hasten toward death. If it comes before I shall have had an opportunity to show all my artistic capacities, it will still come too early for me despite my hard fate, and I shall probably wish that it had come later. But even then I am satisfied. Will it not free me from a state of endless suffering? Come when thou wilt, I shall meet thee bravely.

Farewell and do not wholly forget me when I am dead. I

deserve this of you in having often in life thought of you, how to make you happy. Be so—

LUDWIG VAN BEETHOVEN

(Seal)

Heiglnstadt, October 6th, 1802

For my brothers Carl and ——, to be read and executed after my death.

Heiglnstadt, October 10th, 1802, thus do I take my farewell of thee—and indeed sadly—yea that beloved hope—which I brought with me when I came here to be cured at least in a degree—I must wholly abandon, as the leaves of autumn fall and are withered so hope has been blighted, almost as I came—I go away—even the high courage—which often inspired me in the beautiful days of summer—has disappeared—O Providence, grant me at last but one day of pure *joy*—it is so long since real joy echoed in my heart. Oh, when—Oh, when, O Divine One—shall I feel it again in the temple of nature and of men. Never? No— oh, that would be too hard.

A few days later, Beethoven returned to Vienna, and there, perhaps because the writing of the will had helped to relieve the pent-up feelings of his heart, perhaps as a result of his long quiet months in the country, his health began to improve.

Then, quite by chance one day, he ran across Stephan von Breuning on the street.

"Stephan!" he cried brokenly, all memory of their quarrel vanishing. "How I have missed you these many months!"

Beethoven could not do enough to compensate for his previous ill humor. He racked his brain to think of some way in which to make amends.

On his desk lay a beautiful miniature painted on ivory which had been presented to him by the artist Hornemann. It was the best picture that had ever been made of Beethoven, and he decided to send it to Stephan as a peace offering. He sat down and wrote an impulsive note to his old friend.

Let us bury behind this picture forever, my dear Stephan, all that for a time *passed between us.* I know that I broke your heart. The feelings within me which you must have noticed have sufficiently punished me for that. It was not *wickedness* that I felt towards you. No, if that were so I should never again be worthy of your friendship. Passion on *your part* and *on mine.* But mistrust of you arose in me; men came between us who are not worthy of *you* and *me.* My portrait was long ago intended for you; you know that I always intended it for somebody. To whom could I give it with so warm a heart as to you, faithful, good, noble Stephan! Forgive me if I have pained you; I suffered no less. When I no longer saw you near me, I felt for the first time how dear to *my* heart you are and always will be.

Surely you will come to my arms again as in past days!

When he had finished the note he called his servant to him. "Take this letter and package to Herr Stephan von Breuning on the Hohenstrasse," he said.

For the first time in months Beethoven felt light-hearted again. He set himself with a steady determination to overcome every obstacle in his way. And now began the most productive period of his entire career. During the following six years he wrote a succession of his greatest masterpieces.

CHAPTER XIV

THE *EROICA*

(1 8 0 3 - 1 8 0 4)

A T DAYBREAK, one morning in early April 1803, young
Ferdinand Ries was awakened by a violent knocking at his door.

"Herr van Beethoven requests that you come to him
immediately," the master's servant informed him.

Ries rubbed the sleep from his eyes and threw on his

clothes. When he reached Beethoven's lodgings he found the master sitting up in bed, writing furiously. The floor was covered with pages from his new oratorio, *The Mount of Olives*,* which was to be given that same evening.

"Is that you, Ferdinand?" he called fretfully. "I need your help." He pointed to the scattered sheets. "I decided suddenly in the night that the aria, '*Erzittre, Erde,*' needs a trombone accompaniment. And now," he exclaimed with irritation, "there is the devil of a rush to get it ready in time!"

Ries knew Beethoven too well to object, though he thought it would be impossible to finish the work in time for the rehearsal at eight o'clock that morning. But he set himself diligently to the task, and with their combined efforts the parts were finally written out. Shortly after eight o'clock they hurried to the waiting orchestra.

Prince Lichnowsky, who made it a point to be present at the rehearsals of Beethoven's new compositions, had already arrived. "This will be the finest concert you have ever given!" he said with enthusiasm. "Two symphonies,† the *Christus,* and the new concerto ‡ all in one evening— what a treat!"

Beethoven smiled at him with affection. How different

* *Christus am Oelberge.*
† The First, in C major (Opus 21), and the Second, in D major (Opus 36).
‡ The Third Piano Concerto, in C minor (Opus 37).

his career might have been without the liberal help and warm friendship of Prince Lichnowsky!

The rehearsal began at once, but it proved unusually difficult: the trombone players had trouble with the new parts, the singers were temperamental, and Beethoven, already worn out by his night of work, was impossible to please.

By two o'clock the entire company was ready to give up, and if it hadn't been for Prince Lichnowsky the rehearsal would have ended then and there. With his usual thoughtfulness the Prince, when he saw how things were going, sent out to get food for the weary musicians, and before long his servants arrived bearing large baskets of bread and butter, cold meat, and wine.

"Now let's try the oratorio once more," he begged when everyone felt rested and sufficiently refreshed. They started again with renewed energy, and at last the rehearsal went smoothly.

When evening came, the Theater-an-der-Wien was packed with eager listeners. *The Mount of Olives* was Beethoven's first attempt at sacred music, and the music lovers of Vienna were looking forward to it with much interest.

The new oratorio had only a fair success, though the trombone accompaniment, which Beethoven and Ries had written out only that morning, was commended. The correspondent of a music magazine wrote that *Christus am Oelberge* contained "a few admirable passages—an air of the 'Seraph' with trombone accompaniment in particular producing an admirable effect."

After the oratorio came the new concerto. "You must turn the pages for me," Beethoven told Seyfried, director of the Opera orchestra, as he sat down to play the piano part.

Seyfried looked the score over anxiously. He saw almost nothing but empty leaves, with here and there a hiero-glyphic to remind the master of his part.

"How can you expect—" the man began, but Beethoven cut him short.

"Never mind, I didn't have time to write it out, but I can manage."

Seyfried still looked perplexed, wondering how he should know when to turn the pages.

"I'll nod my head when you must turn," Beethoven whispered with a chuckle and signaled to the orchestra to begin.

Seyfried was still concerned. Surely not even the cele-brated Beethoven could play a whole concerto from an empty score! But the master knew what he was about, and his remarkable memory carried him through without failing. The new concerto was received with great applause.

Two more piano concertos followed the C Minor—the Fourth, in 1805, and the famous *Emperor* in 1809. By this time Beethoven was too deaf to play in public. Moreover, except for an occasional sonata, he wrote no further works for the piano.

A month later, Ries was again summoned at four-thirty in the morning.

"Here!" cried Beethoven distractedly. "Be a good fellow and copy this violin part as fast as you can. I promised to write a new sonata for Bridgetower to play at his concert, but I simply wasn't able to get at it until just a few days ago."

The master himself had agreed to accompany the violinist. There were only a few scratches on the piano pages, but that didn't worry Beethoven; he was used to deciphering his own musical shorthand.

While Ries was furiously copying out the violin part, in walked George Bridgetower, a famous mulatto violinist— son of an "African Prince" (as his father was called in London) and a Polish mother. His concert was scheduled for eight o'clock that very morning, and he had not even seen the music of Beethoven's that he was to play.

But thanks to the amazing skill of both performers, the

violin sonata (in A, Opus 47) went off in fine form. The Andante—which became one of Beethoven's best-loved melodies—made such an impression that it had to be repeated.

Andante

Kreutzer Sonata for violin and piano, slow movement, Andante con variazione

Before Bridgetower left Vienna, he and the master quarreled, and instead of inscribing the sonata to the mulatto, Beethoven dedicated it to the violinist Rudolph Kreutzer. But Kreutzer never played the composition that was to make his name famous—he called it "unintelligible."

The *Kreutzer* Sonata was sent to Simrock, Beethoven's old friend in Bonn, for publication. For some reason Simrock was very slow in bringing out the work, and Beethoven finally sent him a humorous reminder:

Dear, best Simrock: I have been waiting with longing for the sonata I gave you, but in vain. Please write me what the condition of affairs is concerning it—whether or not you accepted it from me merely as food for moths. . . . Where in hiding is this slow devil who is to drive out the sonata? Or what kind of devil is it that sits on my sonata and with whom *you* have a misunderstanding? Hurry, then, and tell me when I shall see the sonata given to the light of day. . . .

Beethoven was notorious for finishing his commissions at the last possible minute. His other famous violin work, the Concerto (Opus 61), was also played without previous rehearsal and with the ink still wet on the score. This concerto was dedicated to his closest friend—Stephan von Breuning, and later the composer made a transcription for piano which he inscribed to Stephan's mother, Frau Hélène von Breuning, who had been so good to him in the years of his youth.

It was the custom in Beethoven's day for a composer to dedicate a work either to the person who had commissioned it, or in the hope of securing the aid of some wealthy patron. For this reason the names of Beethoven's personal friends seldom appear on his music. In one instance at least, however, a dedication served a double purpose. To Count von Waldstein, who during those early days in Bonn had been both patron and friend, the master inscribed one of his finest piano sonatas. Together with the *Appassionata,* the *Pathétique,* and the *Sonata quasi una fantasia* in C sharp minor (the "Moonlight"), the *Waldstein* (Opus 53) has proved the most popular of all the thirty-two piano sonatas. Its first movement closes with a coda beginning:

Waldstein Sonata, coda of the first movement

When Beethoven first played the new work for his pupil Ries and old Krumpholz, they were both transported. The Andante movement impressed them specially. "But it's too long and important to be in a sonata," Krumpholz insisted. "You should publish it as a separate number."

"Please, master, play it for us again!" Ries urged. This slow movement made such an impression on Beethoven's young disciple that a few hours later, happening to stop by at Prince Lichnowsky's, he was able to repeat it from memory.

The Prince, in his turn captivated by the melody, decided to play a joke on the composer. He forgot that

Beethoven liked to poke fun at others, but was not very gracious in accepting jokes directed at himself. The next day the Prince called on the master.

"I have a little composition here that's not too bad," he began affably.

Beethoven shot him a suspicious glance. He was wary of amateur composers. Their stuff was usually not worth listening to.

"Wouldn't you like to hear it?" the Prince went on.

"No!" said the composer gruffly, turning back to his desk.

But the Prince sat down at the piano and began to play. Beethoven stopped suddenly in his work, turned and listened, then with a leap he reached the piano. "Where did you hear that?" he bellowed. Lichnowsky chuckled and went on playing.

"I know!" the angry master fumed. "It was that rascal Ries with his confoundedly clever memory. He made me play it for him twice. But I'll get even with him! Never again will he hear me, the traitor."

Beethoven was true to his word: from that day on he refused ever to allow Ferdinand Ries to listen to him play. But he did remove the Andante movement from the *Waldstein* and later published it separately under the title *Andante Favori* (Opus 170).

"I am not satisfied with my work so far," Beethoven said to his friend Stephan von Breuning one day in that same spring of 1803. "From this day I mean to make a fresh start."

"Not satisfied?" Stephan exclaimed. "What of your two symphonies?—and the concertos?—and the sonatas?—and the *Christus?*" He stopped for breath. "Why, man, you're *famous!*"

"Old stuff," Beethoven insisted. "Too much of Haydn and Mozart in them. Not enough originality."

Breuning roared with laughter. "But that's what they are always criticizing you for—too much originality. Have you forgotten what they said about the opening chord of your First Symphony? *That* was a daring novelty, if ever there was one! And what about the Scherzo in the Second Symphony? Nothing like that in the old masters. *They* all thought they had to write a solemn minuet for their third movement, and here you come along and give them a 'musical joke' instead."

But Beethoven was hardly listening. "I have an idea now for something very different," he told his friend. "A heroic symphony. . . . Look—" He pulled a sheet of music from his writing table.

Stephan gave a start of surprise as he saw, written in bold letters across the sheet,

BUONAPARTE

Napoleon Bonaparte, general of the French armies and First Consul of France, was the great man of the day. Beethoven admired tremendously the independent spirit and proud courage of the "Little Corporal," feeling that here was a kindred soul who, like himself, despised worldly fame and rank and believed only in the worth of the individual. Just as Bonaparte (or Buonaparte, as the name was spelled originally) would lead the world to a new freedom, so Beethoven hoped to lead music to a more independent eloquence and a freer beauty of form. He now decided to write a symphony in tribute to the great French conqueror.

Beethoven had spoken truly when he said that he intended to "make a fresh start." This new symphony was as different from his two earlier ones as if it had been composed by another man. It was like a gigantic canvas describing the character and achievement of a mighty hero. Not content with substituting a Scherzo for the traditional "Minuet" movement, in this case he also turned the Andante into a Funeral March. The symphony was far longer, too, than any that had so far been written by any composer. But when someone remarked on this to Beethoven, he said arrogantly, "If *I* write a symphony an hour long, it will be found short enough!"

When the Third Symphony was first played, few were able to appreciate its grandeur. At the first performance someone in the gallery called out: "I'll give another kreutzer if the thing will only stop!" Others saw in it "an untamed striving for originality which . . . failed, however, to achieve in any of its parts beauty or true sublimity and power." When one critic stated that the new symphony ("in reality a tremendously expanded, daring, and wild fantasia") often lost itself in lawlessness, and contained much that was "glaring and bizarre," the master only laughed.

"Yes," he said, "they marvel and put their heads together and search through all the books. But they will never find these things in any textbook on thoroughbass."

In May 1804, just after the score of the Third Symphony had been completed, Beethoven was at home talking with Count Moritz Lichnowsky, brother of Prince Carl, when Ferdinand Ries burst into the room.

"Napoleon!" he began, still gasping from his hurried climb up the long stairs.

"Young man," said Beethoven sharply, "you'll ruin your lungs if you aren't more careful. What is it now?"

"Napoleon has declared himself Emperor of the French!"

The composer stared at him incredulously. *"What?"* he cried. "But he was only elected First Consul! I don't believe that he would seize supreme power like that!"

"But it's true," Ries insisted, thrusting a newspaper under his master's nose. "Here—read about the great ceremonies of his coronation."

As Beethoven read, his expression of incredulity turned to bitter contempt. Then, when he realized the full significance of Napoleon's action—that betrayal of the ideals of true democracy—he became furiously angry.

"I thought Buonaparte was a hero," he cried indignantly, "but he's really nothing more than an ordinary human being! Now he will trample on the rights of man and indulge only his ambition. He will exalt himself above all others—become a tyrant. . . ."

With a sudden fierce gesture Beethoven seized the manuscript of the new symphony dedicated to Napoleon, tore the title page across, and threw the whole thing on the floor.

The others cried out in dismay. Young Ries started to pick up the scattered sheets, but the master stopped him. "Leave it—" he said.

Count Moritz tried to reason with him. "Your work is far greater than the man who inspired it," he said earnestly.

"No one need know for whom it was written. Give it a new title. . . ."

Beethoven stared moodily at the floor. "I might call it the *Eroica*," he said with grim humor. "Its Funeral March will mourn the passing of *my* hero."

This stately dirge of Beethoven's Third Symphony is the noblest funeral march ever written. Through its somber measures sounds the heavy tramp of marching feet like the relentless fate which pursues man from the cradle to the grave, and which not even a Hero can escape.

Symphony No. 3, Eroica, *second movement, the Funeral March*

Beethoven's *Eroica* has conquered greater worlds than ever did Napoleon with all his vast armies. And while Bonaparte's huge empire soon disintegrated, as do the ill-gotten gains of all dictators, this mighty symphony has gone on through the ages winning the hearts of men and inspiring them to a more heroic way of life.

CHAPTER XV

FIDELIO

(1 8 0 5 - 1 8 0 6)

HAVE YOU EVER THOUGHT of writing an opera, Herr van Beethoven?" asked Baron Braun, director of the Royal Imperial Theater in Vienna.

Beethoven hesitated a moment before answering. Although he had a natural genius for expressing the dramatic, he was not sure that music for the theater appealed to him. At the same time he realized that most of the Viennese preferred opera to any other form of music, and it would be to his advantage to have a stage production.

"Remember Mozart's success with his *Marriage of Figaro,* and *The Magic Flute,* and *Don Giovanni*," the Baron continued persuasively. "If a suitable libretto could be found for you . . . ?"

At various times Beethoven considered subjects for operas. Among these subjects were Romeo and Juliet (a scene from the Shakespeare play inspired the Andante of the First String Quartet), Alfred the Great, the Founding of Pennsylvania, Romulus and Remus, Macbeth, and others just as diverse. But none of them was just what he wanted. Recently, however, he had come across a poem called *Leonore, or Conjugal Love,* the story of a heroic wife who, disguised as a boy (Fidelio), goes to rescue her unjustly imprisoned husband (Florestan). Beethoven felt a tender reverence for "conjugal love"—though he himself was never to know the blessings of married life—and he finally decided to make an opera of Leonore. Under the name *Fidelio,* the work was scheduled for first performance at the Theater-an-der-Wien on November 20, 1805.

The moment was unfortunately chosen, however. Just a few days before this, Vienna was thrown into an uproar by Napoleon's victorious army, which marched into the city and took possession. Most of Beethoven's aristocratic friends fled into the country, and, when *Fidelio* was played in spite of the general confusion, the theater audience was largely made up of French officers, who at best cared little for German music.

The opera started off to a bad beginning. It was too long; there had not been enough rehearsals; the overture was too difficult for the wood winds, and the singers were not equal to their exacting parts. After three performances, it was withdrawn. Beethoven's friends then suggested that he shorten his score and revise some of the singers' parts. But he obstinately refused to make any changes.

Princess Lichnowsky was the only one who could ever make the composer listen to reason. "Can't you persuade our stubborn hothead to revise his opera?" the Prince asked her.

"Perhaps if he were to hear it sung again, he might see for himself what changes ought to be made," she replied.

"That is an excellent suggestion, my dear!" the Prince exclaimed. "We will arrange to have the singers gather here some evening and go through the music for our Beethoven. Perhaps the new tenor, Herr Röckel, will take the part of Florestan. I hear that he has a fine voice."

When Beethoven arrived at the Lichnowsky palace on the evening arranged for the performance, he sat quietly in a corner to listen, while the Princess herself played the score.

At the end of the second act Lichnowsky turned eagerly to Beethoven. "Can't you see that these two acts need shortening?" he exclaimed, hoping that the master had noted how restless the company had grown.

Beethoven shook his head with stubborn dignity. "No, I can't see anything that should be omitted," he said firmly.

The Prince insisted. "Make one act instead of two," he pleaded. "Let your friend Breuning revise the score. Leave out this—and this—"

"Not a note, not a note must be taken out!" Beethoven exclaimed in deep offense. He closed the score with a bang and started toward the door.

"Wait!" the Princess cried. She clasped him gently by the arm and looked up at him with earnest pleading.

"Beethoven," she said, sighing deeply, "must your great work continue to be misunderstood?"

He stared at her with a troubled frown. Suddenly her frail figure became filled with power.

"No, Beethoven, no!" she cried, clasping her hands together in supplication. "You *must* give in! God, who gave you the power to express such divine music, commands it. Your mother who speaks through my voice and pleads with you commands it likewise." She looked up at him like one inspired. "Do this in memory of your mother— do it for me, for I am your true friend!"

Beethoven was profoundly moved by the Princess's entreaties. He stood a moment irresolute, then threw his head up proudly. "Very well, I will!" he exclaimed with emotion. "Yes, it shall be as you desire!" His voice trembled. "For your sake—for my mother's sake, I will do as you say!"

As Beethoven made the important decision a great sigh of relief swept over the company. It had been to the deep regret of Beethoven's admirers that this one effort in the field of opera had not met with success.

Princess Lichnowsky started the first act of *Fidelio* once more, and the master began to see what changes should be made.

Röckel pleased him particularly in the role of Florestan, and Beethoven made him repeat the great aria *"In des Lebens Frühlingstagen"* again and again while he himself noted down the changes that were needed.

The performance lasted until well after midnight, and when finally the great doors into the sumptuous dining-room were opened and the visitors went in to the banquet prepared for them, they were well able to do justice to Prince Lichnowsky's hospitality.

Beethoven sat opposite the new tenor and talked to him with rare good humor.

"You eat like a famished wolf," he said jovially to Röckel.

The tenor laughed. "It is no wonder, sir, since I missed my tea this afternoon."

Beethoven threw back his head and laughed. "It is not surprising, then, that you were able to sing the part of the starving Florestan so convincingly! Hereafter you should always fast before you sing Florestan!"

The whole table joined in the laughter that followed, while the Princess pressed Beethoven's hand affectionately, rejoicing to see him in good spirits once more after his long period of gloom and discouragement.

Beethoven first set to work on the overture. Instead of merely changing the part that had proved too difficult for the wood winds, he decided to write something entirely new. To him, as to most composers, the overture was the most important part of the whole opera. It must not only serve as an introduction and a synopsis of the themes and the action to follow, but—according to Beethoven's ideas

—it should also be a dramatic interpretation of the characters' temperaments and the ideals for which they were striving.

The new overture succeeded so well in achieving these things that, like Jack's beanstalk, it grew out of all ordinary bounds, and Beethoven soon realized that it was much too important to use merely as a prelude to an opera. Known as the *Leonore Overture No. 3,* it later became one of the master's most popular symphonic works.*

At the last minute Beethoven tossed off another, lighter piece to serve as overture for *Fidelio;* then, a year or two later, still another. In all, four overtures for this opera were written, each a separate and distinct composition.

It was through Beethoven's struggles with the various *Leonore* overtures that he discovered a new form of music. He never wrote another opera, but the dramatic overtures

Turkish March *from The Ruins of Athens*

he wrote for the plays *Coriolanus, Egmont, The Ruins of Athens,* and others were forerunners of a type of compo-

---

* An amusing story is told in connection with the trumpet solo that is played offstage in this overture—signaling the arrival of Florestan's rescuers. At a concert in New York City some years ago, the trumpeter had just begun his solo from the wings, when the janitor happened to come by. He

sition developed in the nineteenth century and very popular ever since then—the tone poem.

The following spring—1806—*Fidelio* was produced in
its revised form, and this time it met with better success;
those who were true musicians hailed it as a masterpiece.
But the attendance was limited, and the theater scarcely
half filled. After the third performance, Beethoven went
over to see Baron Braun.

"I can't understand why *Fidelio* is not more successful,"
he said impatiently. The Baron remarked that Beethoven's
music did not appeal to the multitudes, who brought in
the money.

"I do not write for the multitudes!" Beethoven exclaimed, walking up and down the room in great agitation.

"Then you have only yourself to blame if your receipts
are small," the Baron answered with superior politeness.
"Mozart didn't scorn to write for the less cultured people."

Thunder gathered on Beethoven's brow. "Give me back
my score!" he cried angrily. The Baron looked at him a

seized the musician by the shoulder. "You can't do that!" he cried indignantly. "Don't you know there's a concert going on in there?"

moment in surprise. "My score, at once!" Beethoven repeated, his face glowing with passion.

Baron Braun pulled the bell rope and turned with dignity to his servant. "Bring the score of *Fidelio* to this gentleman," he said coldly.

When the servant returned a few moments later, Beethoven tore the heavy volume from his hands and without another word rushed from the room.

The Baron stared after him in dismay. Then he called into an adjoining room where Herr Röckel, the tenor, was waiting for him.

"This is a pretty predicament," he exclaimed with vexation. "How shall we continue our performance now?"

"Perhaps I could persuade him to change his mind," Röckel began.

Baron Braun seized the man's hat and thrust it into his hands. "Go and try—there's a good fellow. Promise him anything!"

But all of Röckel's pleadings were in vain. Beethoven was too deeply wounded. That his great work had been twice misunderstood! Even Stephan von Breuning, who had helped him to revise the score, could not persuade the master to relinquish it again. He put it away in a dark corner of his manuscript closet, and it did not appear again until eight years later, when in 1814 finally it was presented with complete triumph.

Breuning wrote to his sister Lorchen about the opera.

Nothing else, perhaps, has caused Beethoven so much vexation as this work, the value of which will be appreciated only in the future. . . . I remodeled the whole book for him, quickening and enlivening the action; he curtailed many pieces, and then it was performed three times with great success. However, his enemies in the theater rose, and, as he had offended several persons, especially at the second performance, they succeeded in preventing further performances. . . . This is all the more unpleasant for Beethoven, since the cessation of the performances on which he was depending for his honorarium—a percentage of the receipts—has embarrassed him financially. He will recover from the set-back all the more slowly since the treatment he has received has robbed him of a great deal of his pleasure in, and love for, work. . . .

Beethoven was greatly discouraged when he figured up his accounts. He had hoped the opera would bring him in a considerable sum of money, and now there was nothing more to be expected from it.

To the praise of Thy goodness I must confess that Thou hast tried all means to draw me to Thee. Now it hath pleased Thee to let me feel the heavy hand of Thy wrath, and to humiliate my proud heart by manifold chastisements. Sickness and misfortune hast Thou sent to bring me to a contemplation of my digressions. But one thing only do I ask, O God, cease not to labor for my improvement. Only let me, in whatsoever manner pleaseth Thee, turn to Thee and be fruitful of good works.

These words, which Beethoven read in a book by Christian Sturm, appealed to him so strongly that he made a copy of the passage in his *Tagebuch,* or journal. Now, instead of "recovering slowly from the set-back" of *Fidelio,* as Stephan von Breuning had feared, he turned from the past and became "fruitful of good works." To him, discouragement only acted as a spur to greater effort. Immediately following his opera's second failure, Beethoven began work on what is perhaps his greatest piano sonata, the *Appassionata,* and also on the string quartets called *Rasumowsky* (the three quartets in Opus 59).

Count Andreas Rasumowsky, ambassador to Austria from the court of Russia, was a man of large fortune and a liberal patron of all the arts. His beautiful palace in Vienna was filled with priceless paintings and sculpture, and contained a large library of rare books. Some time later a fire broke out in this palace (it was during a lavish entertainment for the visiting Czar of Russia, where dinner was served to seven hundred guests) and most of the Count's treasures were destroyed. He never recovered from the shock.

Rasumowsky was married to the Princess Lichnowsky's

sister, and he had been one of the first subscribers to Beethoven's music (the three Trios, Opus 1). He himself was an excellent violinist, and his favorite recreation was to play quartets with his own group of musicians. He had long wanted Beethoven to compose some chamber music for this group. Finally he commissioned him to write three string quartets.

"Could you bring in some Russian melodies?" he asked, remembering the colorful melodies of his homeland.

Beethoven bowed. "There shall be one of your native folk songs in each quartet," he promised. The most famous of the folk melodies thus used is the one found in the second Rasumowsky Quartet—the same tune that the Russian composer Mussorgsky was later to use in the Coronation Scene of *Boris Godunov*.

Second Rasumowsky Quartet, Opus 59, No. 2, Thème russe

When the *Fidelio* fiasco drove Beethoven to new composition, he turned to writing these quartets for Count Rasumowsky. Several preliminary sketches had already been set down. Perhaps because of his recent disappointment, he now seemed determined to show his defiance of old rules and traditions. At any rate, when the first of the quartets was tried out at Count Rasumowsky's home, with Schuppanzigh playing first violin, the four players didn't know what to make of it. The first few bars of the first movement—all on one note until the real melody enters —made them burst into laughter.

First Rasumowsky Quartet, Opus 59, No. 1, first movement

"What crazy music is this?" exclaimed the Count, frowning. "Surely this is not the quartet Beethoven promised me!"

Schuppanzigh's fat face creased into a chuckle. "It's just another of his jokes. . . . But I don't see why he had to make the violin part so complicated."

Others who heard the music were even more incensed. "Patchwork by a madman!" they cried. The music-publisher Gyrowetz took the quartets on the strength of Beethoven's reputation, but when he looked them over he was dismayed. "Pity to waste the money," he grumbled.

"Everyone says—and I agree—that Beethoven is music-mad, for these are not music," said an Italian violinist named Radicati. When the master asked him to finger the violin parts to the Rasumowsky quartets, he made the same remark to the composer himself. "Surely you don't consider these to be *music?*"

Beethoven looked at the man haughtily. "Those weren't written for you. They are for a later age. . . ."

When he heard that Schuppanzigh had complained about the difficulty of some of the passages, he only shrugged his shoulders. "Does he imagine that I think of his silly fiddle when the spirit speaks to me and I compose?"

Today the Rasumowsky Quartets do not strike us as being radical at all. Though in sharp contrast to the earlier ones (Opus 18), still, as compared with the great "last quartets," they seem almost conventional in form. It is hard for us to realize how revolutionary Beethoven's music must have sounded to his contemporaries. In every age the composer of genius, with something original to say, has had to battle against tradition-bound listeners who, because the music is new and different, cannot understand it, and therefore condemn it. Much that today offends our ears may, like the "heresies" in Beethoven's audacious compositions, sound right and even commonplace to future generations.

Carl van Beethoven sauntered into his brother's lodgings, walked casually around the room, and looked over Beethoven's shoulder at the music he was writing.

"I have made arrangements to send your three new sonatas to Hofmeister in Leipzig," he remarked.

Beethoven looked up quickly from his writing.

"Hofmeister!" he exclaimed, frowning. "Why, you know that I have already promised them to Nägeli in Zurich." He surveyed his brother with increasing anger. "I'm glad you came in this morning." He rose abruptly and waved some printed sheets of music in the other's face. "What is the meaning of this?"

Carl shifted his gaze. "Why, that is just a little service I have done for you, Ludwig," he said affably. "I spent some time in gathering together those fragments for publication."

"*Fragments,* indeed!" Beethoven exploded. "How dare you publish things without my knowledge? Trash I wrote when I was a youth—worthless—not fit to appear under my name!" He approached his brother angrily. "You meddle too much in my affairs, you and Johann. I suppose you think I have not noticed how you have been trying to keep my friends away. And now this outrageous piece of presumption!"

Carl retreated toward the door and placed his hand on the knob. "I needed the money badly, Ludwig," he pleaded.

His brother snorted in disdain, but Carl began to see signs of forgiveness in his expression. Then suddenly Beethoven caught sight of a ring on the hand that held the knob.

"*What!*" he cried, fairly choking with wrath. "Do you even help yourself to my *gifts,* the ring the Emperor gave me!" He started toward Carl furiously, but the latter did not wait for him. He tore the ring from his finger, threw it at his brother's feet, and precipitately fled from the room.

A few days later a Vienna newspaper printed the following announcement:

This 25th of May, 1806, a marriage contract was closed between Carl Caspar van Beethoven, R. I. Officer of the Revenue, and of this city [Vienna], and Theresia Reiss, daughter of Anton Reiss, civilian, upholsterer.

Beethoven scowled angrily as he read the notice of his brother's marriage. Carl had not consulted him—he knew better, for the reputation of the new sister-in-law was only too well known to Beethoven.

"Bah!" he exclaimed. "That ends the matter. I shall have nothing further to do with them." At the time he could think only of the indignity to his family pride. Little did he realize what far-reaching consequences this marriage was to have on his life.

CHAPTER XVI

"V FOR VICTORY"

(1 8 0 7 - 1 8 0 8)

T HE COUNTESS VON BRUNSWICK tapped her heel sharply against the floor of her sitting-room in the Golden Dragon. "Surely, Franz," she said with a touch of irritation, "since you have known Herr van Beethoven for so long, you should be able to persuade him to give lessons to Therese."

224

Franz von Brunswick shook his handsome head doubtfully. It was true that he had known the composer since his earliest days in Vienna, when he and Schuppanzigh played his trios at the home of the Baron Zmeskall. But of late years Beethoven had shut himself away from everyone, and it was very difficult to approach him.

"You don't realize how eccentric he has become," Brunswick answered slowly. "It's almost impossible to persuade him to teach anyone now. He refuses everyone in order to have more time for composing."

"But since Therese is your sister and she has been counting so eagerly on having some lessons with him during our short stay here?" his mother insisted.

Franz smiled and shrugged his shoulders; he knew that such arguments would have no effect on a man who lived only to create music. Yet Brunswick was sorry to disappoint his sister. Therese was a charming girl, and she admired Beethoven ardently. This visit to Vienna from their country place at Martonvasar would not be complete unless the great musician had a part in it.

"Perhaps if you went to Beethoven yourself," Franz said, looking at Therese reflectively, "he might consider. It all depends upon the mood you find him in. And it's true," his eyes twinkled mischievously, "that the master has a weakness for pretty faces!"

Therese protested with a blush, but she responded at

once to the idea. "Do let's try it, Mamma!" she exclaimed, clasping her hands together.

"Why, Therese, what are you thinking of!" the Countess answered in a shocked voice. "To run after a common, ordinary musician!"

"He is neither common nor ordinary," Brunswick remonstrated warmly. "Even princes look up to him, and the Emperor himself has shown Beethoven special favor. In spite of his strange manners he has a fine character. And his music—could anyone be his equal *there?*"

"Ah, well," his mother replied with resignation, "if it means so much to you, Therese, I am willing to sacrifice myself. And," she continued meekly, "to please you, I will even climb all those dreadful stairs that lead to the music eagle's nest!"

Therese embraced her affectionately and ran to get her music. "Now . . . we must go at once!" she cried.

Fortunately the "music eagle" had not flown when they reached his lodgings, and after a short wait in the anteroom, Beethoven came in to them with outstretched hands.

"Franz von Brunswick's mother and sister are always welcome!" he exclaimed with pleasure. "How good of you to call on me!" He looked at Therese with admiration. "I see you are musical, Fräulein." He pointed to the music she held. "Like your gifted brother, no doubt."

Therese stammered a few words in reply, and tried to

tell him how much *his* music meant to her. He listened
intently, his hand to his ear, and finally Frau von Brunswick came to her rescue.

"Therese has been hoping above everything that you
would give her a few lessons," she said in a loud voice,
watching Beethoven's face hopefully.

He ran his fingers through his thick black hair and
looked again at the lovely girl before him.

"It would be a pleasure," he murmured politely, "but
unfortunately I am in the midst of a new overture for
Fidelio just at present. . . ." He stared a moment at the
floor. Then as he looked up he saw the pleading in Therese's eyes.

An engaging smile suddenly lit up his dark face. He
took the girl by the hand and led her gently to the piano.

"I shall manage it some way, Fräulein," he said softly.
There was a stirring in his heart such as he had not known
since Giulietta became the bride of Count von Gallenberg.

Each day after this, in spite of his work on the revision
of the opera, Beethoven found time to go to the Golden
Dragon and give Therese a lesson. Instead of remaining
for an hour, he would often stay until late in the after-

noon, regardless of the inconvenience to himself and to them.

By the time Therese was ready to leave Vienna, his interest in the girl had grown to an unusual degree. He was always falling in love, but this time he began to wonder if at last he had found the ideal of his dreams. He felt the girl's sympathy and understanding; he had been so often wounded, however, that he did not dare allow himself to hope for her love.

Therese was now more firmly convinced than ever that the majesty of Beethoven's music sprang from the depths of a noble heart. She felt a strange reluctance at the thought of leaving Vienna. "If you are traveling this summer, could you not visit us at Martonvasar?" she begged the master. Franz added his appeal, and even the Countess graciously insisted.

"It would give me great joy," he answered. "I will surely come—if only"—his face clouded—"this new presentation of *Fidelio* is a success and helps to fill my empty pockets!"

Unfortunately, however, *Fidelio* fared no better in its revised form than it had the first time it was given. Beethoven wondered how he would get to Martonvasar—and Therese.

Prince Lichnowsky realized what a disappointment the failure of *Fidelio* had meant to the composer. He half suspected also that the latter's finances were seriously affected by the loss.

"Beethoven will probably be unable to afford a stay in the country this summer," the Princess said. "Why not invite him to come here with us?"

Prince Lichnowsky wrote immediately and suggested that the musician spend the summer months with them at their country seat in Silesia.

A short time later, as Therese von Brunswick was starting off on her favorite chestnut mare through the park at Martonvasar, her brother appeared at the door waving a letter in his hand.

"Beethoven is coming!" he shouted from the top of the steps.

Therese put her hand to her heart and grew suddenly pale. *"Soon?"* she called back.

"He should be here this very day," Franz replied, consulting the letter again. "He is planning to stop off on his way to Silesia to visit Prince Lichnowsky."

Therese leapt from her horse and threw the reins to the waiting groom. She was suddenly all energetic action and flushed concern.

"The tower room must be prepared for him at once," she said with decision. "He will be sure to want a piano; the one in the lower drawing-room shall be moved to the tower, and he can have all the quiet he needs for his work."

She hurried into the house to inform her mother and make the necessary preparations, while Franz ordered the carriage to meet the stagecoach from Vienna.

When Beethoven arrived, a few hours later, he was cordially received by all the family. Franz prepared to appropriate his friend for himself—though the composer plainly had eyes for no one but Therese—but for the moment Beethoven was too preoccupied with his new sonata to think of anything but his work. Therese, hovering near the tower room, heard wonderful music being played.

The sonata was finished in record time. "I have dedicated it to you, Franz," he said. "It is to be called the *Appassionata.*" *

Sonata Appassionata, Opus 57, second movement

* In 1809 Beethoven again dedicated one of his great piano works to Franz von Brunswick—the Fantaisie in G Minor (Opus 77)—while to Therese he inscribed the Sonata in F sharp (Opus 78).

Therese was the first to hear the new "passionate sonata."
"Do you like it, Fräulein Therese?" he asked her.

The girl smiled at him through tears. "It is the most
beautiful thing I ever heard! No one else has ever written
such music!"

Beethoven was accustomed to praise from his friends.
But there was a depth of feeling in Therese's words that
touched his heart. During his stay at Martonvasar he realized that Franz's sister had a gentle spirit and a brilliant
mind as well as a graceful figure. What a wife she would
make for a lonely man, he thought!—then wondered with
quick apprehension whether she would consider his thirty-
six years too old for her, or whether someone else already
held first place in her affections.

The estate of the Brunswicks stretched out in all directions. Beethoven and Therese took long walks together,
wandering through wooded hills and sunlit fields until the
lonely and unhappy man felt joy and happiness flood his
soul once more.

One day Therese took him to an open space planted
with a circle of linden trees whose fragrant blossoms hung
in thick clusters.

"Here is the dwelling place of noble spirits," she said
softly, laying her head against the trunk of one of the trees.

Beethoven stood silent, trying to imagine the hum of
the bees at work among the linden blossoms.

"Each tree, you see, stands for some dear absent friend," Therese went on. "I shall name one for you, Beethoven," she said, raising her blue eyes to his.

He started forward eagerly, his lonely heart full of hope. But the girl didn't notice. She wound her arms about the tree against which she was leaning.

"This dear tree, for instance," she murmured, "how it brings back tender memories . . .!"

Beethoven stopped quickly, and the light went out of his eyes. "Of course . . ." he thought to himself sadly. "I should have known that there were others before me— more worthy of her love than I am."

Aloud he spoke a few broken words of excuse to the astonished Therese, and turned blindly into the forest.

"Fool—donkey—dullhead!" he apostrophized himself as he stumbled through the underbrush. "What have you to offer a wife?" He kicked savagely at a fallen branch in his path. He knew how rigidly social position was observed among the upper classes. "Why should a high-born girl like Therese even think of marrying *me?* No, it is my fate to live alone, unloved. . . ."

As he wandered disconsolately through the forest, a relentless rhythm began to dog his footsteps. The sharp staccato notes seemed to say: "It-is-your-Fate . . . *It-is-your-Fate!*"

"What is the use of going on?" he reflected grimly.

"Fate has marked me for unhappiness. And who can deny the power of that dark force?"

All at once, from overhead there came a clear, melodious call. At first the unhappy man thought he must be imagining it, but then it came again—four brief notes like a joyous echo of the theme that had been pursuing him.

Beethoven looked up in surprise and saw, in the tree above his head, a warbling yellowhammer. Strangely affected, he stood there, silent, his face turned heavenward. Was it the voice of his beloved Nature trying to speak to him?—to tell him that he, too, held within himself the power to change darkness into light?

He reached into his pocket for his pencil and notebook and began to write. And from the brief song of the yellowhammer grew one of the world's greatest symphonies.

From Martonvasar, Beethoven went to Silesia to visit the Lichnowskys. There he found a number of French officers who had quartered themselves in the Prince's country home. Beethoven had never gotten over his resentment at Napoleon's treachery to the ideals he had ascribed to him; each new triumph of the dictator he took as a personal affront. When Bonaparte beat the Prussians at Jena, he cried: "If only I understood the art of war as well as I do the art of music, I would crush him yet!"

At Prince Lichnowsky's, the French officers asked him to play, but the master haughtily refused. Even when the Prince added his request he stubbornly held his ground.

"Come, come," Lichnowsky jokingly insisted. "I am your host, you know, and you must obey me. If you won't play, I'll have to have you locked up. . . ."

Beethoven turned furiously; he was in no mood for a joke. These aristocrats—they thought they owned the world! But no one should tell *him* what to do. He stormed out of the room, gathered his belongings together, and, in spite of the night, walked several miles to the nearest town—Troppau—where he took a special coach to Vienna.

On the way, a heavy rainstorm soaked all his luggage. When he reached his rooms he discovered that the manuscript of his new *Sonata Appassionata* was soaking wet. This was the last straw. Looking about for something on which to vent his anger, he saw a plaster bust of Prince Lichnowsky standing on a cabinet. In childish fury he threw it violently to the floor, where it shattered into a thousand pieces. Then he sat down and wrote the Prince a scathing letter, ending:

What you are, you are by accident of birth; what I am, I am through myself. There have been and will be thousands of princes; there is only one Beethoven. . . .

234

The next summer, in 1807, Beethoven moved out to Heiligenstadt. Five years before, he had there set down his melancholy "Heiligenstadt Will." Now this picturesque village became the birthplace of two of his greatest symphonies—the Fifth, in C Minor, and the Sixth, called the *Pastoral*.

For the Fifth he had ready a number of themes. Beethoven's notebooks show how carefully he worked over his original ideas. If genius is, as someone once said, "the capacity for taking infinite pains," then the master-musician deserves the highest rank. Each of his themes was polished until it became like a jewel, perfect and worthy to include in some masterpiece.

In Heiligenstadt, Beethoven finally completed what has become the world's most famous symphony. For the beginning of the great C Minor he chose four short notes taken (as he later told Czerny) from a yellowhammer's song. "Thus Fate knocks at the door," he said to another friend, and for years this work was known as the *Fate* Symphony.

In these staccato notes it is easy to imagine Fate knocking at the door. But the first audience who listened to the Fifth Symphony thought the opening phrase a joke. Who but Beethoven, they remarked, would dare to start a symphony with such a thin, stupid theme? They were not yet able to understand the master's "miraculous faculty for creating worlds out of nothingness," as Wagner once put it.

More than a century later, these four opening notes of the C Minor Symphony were to become an international symbol. Soon after the outbreak of World War II, hardpressed England adopted as her rallying cry "V for Victory!" Then someone discovered that the opening phrase of Beethoven's Fifth Symphony—

spells the letter "V" in the Morse code. Immediately the C Minor became the "Victory" Symphony, and during the dark hours of the war it was played repeatedly—helping to give men renewed faith in the ultimate power of good over evil.

That this mighty work should have been chosen as a symbol of Victory was particularly fitting. The first movement is like a titanic struggle between the forces of light and darkness, while the last is a majestic hymn to victory. Beethoven himself once said that the C Minor represented "a duel between free will and determinism." If he had lived in the 1940's, he might have said "between freedom and dictatorship."

"Nature was almost meat and drink to Beethoven," a friend of the master's once remarked. "He seemed positively to live on it. . . ."

"No mortal can love the country as I do," Beethoven said to himself as he walked through the woods near Heiligenstadt, that same summer of 1807. To him the forest was like a great cathedral—his place of worship. "Almighty God," he whispered reverently, "in these woods I am blest. Through Thee every tree has a voice, and seems to say to me 'Holy, Holy!' . . . What glory is in such a place! And peace . . . peace to serve Thee!"

Close beside him as he walked, that summer's day near Heiligenstadt, a murmuring brook hurried along its way, rippling over the rocks in a succession of miniature cascades. Years before, Beethoven had written down the softly flowing note of running water—middle C where it was shallow, lower F when it became deeper.

"In the country my unhappy ears no longer torment me," he once confessed. There were even times, in the stillness of complete solitude, away from the noise and confusion of everyday life, when the veil that covered his hearing lifted for a blessed respite. Now, to the master's glad surprise, the sounds of the forest suddenly became clear to him. He heard the monotonous cry of a cuckoo, the call of a quail, and, like a soft accompaniment, the song of the brook.

As Beethoven listened, his heart filled to overflowing, he was caught up into the ecstasy which even as a child he had occasionally experienced. And as always, he thought: "If only I could capture and hold a little of the glory—if only I could set it down in music so that others might hear . . . and understand!"

An ominous roll of thunder brought him sharply back to his immediate surroundings. Like a battle of celestial giants, bolts of lightning and mighty crashes of sound filled the sky. Then came a downpour of rain. But the storm lasted only a short while. As the master started homeward the sky was aglow with the setting sun; while from the distance came the song of a shepherd folding in his flock. After the rough battle of Nature's elements, this plaintive melody sounded to him like a hymn of thanksgiving.

That evening, Beethoven, as was his frequent custom, went to the village tavern. The country band there played the old Austrian dance tunes with such lusty vigor that even his deaf ears could hear them. The crude playing of the village musicians amused him extravagantly—he took peculiar delight in bad music. As the men sawed away at their instruments he would note how sometimes, in the midst of their music, they would fall asleep for a few minutes, then wake up with a start and begin playing again. Tonight the sleep-drunken bassoonist, after a short doze, blew some particularly loud notes—as if to prove that he really hadn't been asleep at all.

Beethoven enjoyed all this heartily. "What a theme for a Scherzo!" he thought. "Some day I'll have to write down some tunes for these boys." This he did, a dozen or so years later. And, as he handed the music over to the incredulous band leader, he remarked that he "had so arranged the dances that one musician after the other could put down his instrument at intervals and take a little rest —or even a nap."

That night in Heiligenstadt, Beethoven sat long before his window, and the experiences of the day began to weave themselves into a pattern of music. A new work gradually took shape in his mind. It should be, he decided, a "pastoral" symphony, dedicated to the joys of Nature. In his notebook he wrote: "Recollections of country life. Something in which the emotions are expressed which are aroused in men by the pleasures of the country."

Soon he had planned an outline for the new symphony:

SINFONIA PASTORALE

1. *Allegro ma non molto*	Awakening of cheerful emotions on arriving in the country.
2. *Andante con moto*	Scene by the brook.
3. *Allegro* (Scherzo)	Peasants' merrymaking.
4. *Allegro*	Thunderstorm. Tempest.
5. *Allegretto*	Shepherd's Hymn. Happy and thankful feeling after the storm.

When Beethoven finally completed his symphony and looked over what he had written, he shook his head. Music had always been to him an *abstract* art—never a means of describing external, objective things. And here, in his *Pastoral* Symphony, he had done just what in the past he had made fun of in others! For weren't the song of the brook, the cuckoo's notes, the storm and the shepherd's hymn, and the country bassoonist all there? He hadn't meant to be so literal. It was the *emotion* that these things aroused in him that he wanted to express, not the actual scenes or objects. Quickly, so that others should not misunderstand his purpose, he wrote at the top of his manuscript: "More an expression of feeling than tone-painting."

Had he known that his *Pastoral* Symphony was to set the fashion for future generations of "program music" composers, Beethoven might never have published the work; for music, he felt, was too high an art to be used for mere image-making.

CHAPTER XVII

BETTINA AND GOETHE

(1810-12)

A FEW MILES OUT of Vienna stands the stately old palace of Schönbrunn—the summer home of the Austrian Emperors. Around it stretch beautiful gardens, green woods, and well-kept parks. In every direction enchanting vistas open up.

In Beethoven's day Schönbrunn was at the height of its

glory. He was allowed to go there whenever he liked, and it was his favorite spot. Here he would wander for hours, seeking inspiration in the shaded alleys of the park or among the flowers.

One afternoon in the late spring of 1810 he walked through the gardens with an attractive young girl by his side. Women, especially young ones, always seemed to his beauty-loving nature like flowers; and Bettina Brentano, with her rose-colored hooped gown and tiny ruffled parasol, was even better to look at than the gardens around them.

The perfume of the hyacinths was bewildering. Bettina looked around with a quick-drawn breath: the beds of flaming tulips—daffodils, narcissus, ranunculus, anemones—all made a riot of color against the delicate green of the new leaves.

"I don't wonder that you love this place!" she exclaimed with enthusiasm.

Beethoven drew her to a winding path through the park. He pointed to a forked tree. "That is my special armchair," he said with a laugh, "my seat of inspiration! The music for *The Mount of Olives* and *Fidelio* came to me while I was sitting there, trying to learn the harmonies of Nature."

Bettina looked at the tree with interest. She was an extraordinary girl—unusually quick to understand and respond. Goethe, the great German poet, had been fascinated by her charm and vivacity, and when Bettina came to Vienna on a visit they wrote to each other frequently.

Beethoven pointed to a distant row of trimmed trees—artificially cut into odd shapes, stiff and ugly in the midst of the natural beauty of the place.

"Now, *there* is something that I cannot abide!" he exclaimed sharply. "Trees shaped up like old hoop petticoats. . . . Artifice—nothing but artifice!" He looked back at the stately trees of the park. "I feel happy only when I am out where Nature is free."

His companion nodded gently—it was almost impossible to talk to the unfortunate man—and they stopped before a pool bordered with purple iris and shaded with drooping willow trees.

Beethoven's thoughts went deeper. "When I open my eyes and look around the world I must sigh, for what I see is so contrary to what I believe!" He looked sadly at Bettina. "I wish that everyone could understand what music really means—could only realize that its revelation is superior even to that of philosophy."

Bettina listened with sympathetic intelligence. Her friendship with Goethe had made her well able to appreciate the thoughts of genius, and Beethoven found himself putting into words many things which he had never before expressed.

"Music is the entry into higher knowledge," he said with conviction. "Those who understand this are freed from the miseries that others drag around with themselves."

The little pool before them reflected the last rays of the sun, and the water lilies began to close their golden cups. Beethoven looked up with a start. "We must get back," he said with regret; "it is growing late." He turned to Bettina impulsively. "Speak to Goethe about me," he exclaimed. "His poems have great power over me. I am stimulated by his language."

They walked back to the carriage in the growing dusk. "Yes," he went on, "Goethe's speech seems to bear in itself the mystery of the harmonies." Beethoven was talking softly now, almost as if he had forgotten his companion. "When I hear his poems I am inspired to create melody in all directions!" He threw out his arms. "I pursue the harmony—see it flying away and disappearing; then I seize it again—I cannot tear myself away from it." His eyes shone with enthusiasm. "I am impelled to multiply it, and at length," he cried triumphantly, "I conquer it— behold, a symphony!"

He looked wistfully at the girl. "I should like to talk to Goethe about this—would he understand me?"

Bettina was carried away with enthusiasm.

"You and Goethe are kindred souls!" she cried, speaking loudly in his ear. "You must meet and learn to know each other."

Bettina wrote to three of her friends about her meeting with Beethoven: to Goethe, to Anton Bihler, and to Prince Pückler-Muskau. To the first she wrote:

When I saw him of whom I shall now speak to you I forgot the whole world, as the world still vanishes when memory recalls the scene—yes, it vanishes. . . . It is Beethoven of whom I now wish to tell you, and who made me forget the world and you. I am still in my nonage, it is true, but I am not mistaken when I say what no one perhaps now understands and believes—that he stalks far ahead of the culture of mankind. . . .

I did not make his acquaintance until the last days of my stay there. I very nearly did not see him at all, for no one wished to take me to meet him, not even those who called themselves his best friends, for fear of his melancholia, which so completely obsesses him that he takes no interest in anything, and treats his friends with rudeness rather than civility. A fantasy he had written, which I heard played in admirable fashion, moved my heart, and from that moment on I felt such a longing that I tried by all means to meet him.

No one knew where he lived, since often he keeps himself altogether secluded. His dwelling place is quite remarkable: In the front room there are from two to three pianos, all legless, lying on the floor; trunks containing his belongings, and a three-legged chair. In the second room is his bed which—winter and summer—consists of a straw mattress and a thin cover; a wash basin on a pinewood table; his nightclothes lying on the floor. Here I waited a good half-hour, for he was shaving at the moment. At last he came in.

In person he was small (for all his soul and heart were so big), brown, and full of pockmarks. He is what one terms repulsive, yet has a divine brow, rounded with such noble harmony that one is tempted to look on it as a magnificent work of art. He has black hair, very long, which he tosses back, and does not know his age, but thinks he is fifty-three.*

I had been told a great deal about how careful one has to be in order not to rouse his ill will; but I had formed quite another estimate of his noble character and had not been mistaken. Within fifteen minutes he felt so kindly toward me that he would not let me go. . . .

This man takes a veritable pride in the fact that he will oblige neither the Emperor nor the Archdukes, who give him a pension, by playing for them, and in all Vienna it is the rarest thing in the world to hear him. Upon my asking him to play he replied: "Well, why should I play?"

"Because I would like to fill my life with all that is most wonderful, and because your playing will be an epoch in my life," I said.

He assured me that he would try to deserve this praise, seated

* Bettina must have misunderstood Beethoven. In 1810, when she first met him, he was forty years old.

himself beside the piano, on the edge of a chair, and played softly with one hand, as though trying to overcome his reluctance to let anyone hear him. Suddenly his surroundings were completely forgotten, and his soul expanded in a universal sea of harmony.

I have become excessively fond of this man. In all that relates to his art he is so dominating and truthful that no other artist can pretend to approach him; with regard to the rest of his life, however, so naïve that one can do with him what one will. His absentmindedness in this last connection has made him a veritable object of ridicule; and he is taken advantage of to such an extent that he seldom has enough money to provide the commonest necessities of life. His friends and brothers make use of him; his clothing is torn, he looks quite out at the elbows, and yet his appearance is noble and imposing.

In addition he is quite hard of hearing and can hardly see. But when he has just composed something he is altogether deaf, and his eyes are confused as they turn toward the outer world: this is because the whole harmony moves on in his brain and his thoughts can busy themselves with nothing else. Hence he is cut off from all that keeps him in touch with the outer world (vision and hearing), so that he lives in the most profound solitude. When one speaks with him at length for a time and stops for a reply, he will suddenly burst forth into tone, draw out his music paper and write. . . .

He kissed my hand and when I was about to leave accompanied me. While we were under way, he said: "Music is the climate of my soul; it is there that it blossoms and does not merely run to seed. Few realize what a throne of passion each single musical movement is—and few know that passion itself is music's throne." And thus he talked, as though I had been his intimate friend for years. . . .

Everyone was surprised to see me enter a company of more than forty persons sitting at the table, hand in hand with the unsociable Beethoven. He took a seat without any demur, saying little, probably because he was deaf. Twice he drew his notebook from his pocket and jotted down a few figures.

After dinner the whole company mounted to the roof tower of the house to enjoy the view of the surroundings. When all had descended again and he and I were alone, he drew out his notebook, glanced over it, wrote and crossed out, and said: "My song is completed." He next leaned from the window and sang it lustily out upon the air. Then he said: "Eh? It sounds, does it not? It belongs to you if you want it. I wrote it for you. You incited me to do so, for I read it in your glance."

Her letter to Anton Bihler contains this paragraph:

Why am I writing you all this in such detail? Because, first of all, I believe that like myself you can understand and esteem such a character; secondly, because I know what injustice is done him, merely because people are too petty to comprehend him. And so I cannot forbear drawing his picture just as I see him.

The following evening she added a few lines to her letter to Goethe:

. . . I promised to write you everything to the best of my understanding. . . . Last night I wrote down all that he [Beethoven] had said; this morning I read it over to him. He remarked: "Did I say that? Well, then I had a 'raptus'!" He read it again attentively and struck out the above and wrote between the lines, for he is greatly desirous that you shall understand him.

Rejoice me now with a speedy answer that will show Beethoven that you appreciate him. It has always been our purpose to discuss music; it was also my desire, but through Beethoven I feel for the first time that I am not fit for the task.

In a few days Goethe's answer came.

. . . Your letter, heartily beloved child, reached me at a happy time. You have been at great pains to picture for me a great and beautiful nature in its achievements and its strivings, its needs and the superabundance of its gifts. It has given me great pleasure to accept this picture of a truly great spirit. . . .

Give Beethoven my heartiest greetings, and tell him I would willingly make sacrifices to have his acquaintance, when an exchange of thoughts and feelings would surely be beautifully profitable. Perhaps you may be able to persuade him to make a journey to Karlsbad, whither I go nearly every year, and where I would have the greatest leisure to listen to him and learn from him. To think of teaching him would be an insolence even in one with greater insight than mine, since he has the guiding light of his genius which frequently illumines his mind like a stroke of lightning, while we sit in darkness and scarcely suspect the direction from which daylight will break upon us.

It would give me great joy if Beethoven were to make me a present of the two songs of mine which he has composed. . . .

I am very eager to hear them. It is one of my greatest enjoyments, for which I am very grateful, to have the old moods of such a poem (as Beethoven very correctly says) newly aroused in me. . . .

Bettina to Goethe:

DEAREST FRIEND!

I communicated your beautiful letter to Beethoven so far as it concerned him. He was full of joy and cried: "If there is anyone who can make him understand music, I am the man!" The idea of hunting you up at Karlsbad filled him with enthusiasm. He struck his forehead a blow and said: "Might I not have done that earlier?—but, in truth, I did think of it but omitted to do it because of timidity, which often torments me as if I were not a real man. But I am no longer afraid of Goethe." You may count, therefore, on seeing him next year. . . .

I am enclosing the two songs by Beethoven; the other two are by me. Beethoven has seen them and said many pretty things about them, such as that if I had devoted myself to this lovely art I might cherish great hopes; but I merely graze it in flight, for my art is only to laugh and sigh in a little pocket—beyond that there is nothing for me. . . .

Two years passed before the meeting between the two masters took place. In 1814, Beethoven, who had been suffering again with poor health, was ordered to the baths at Teplitz, and there at last he found Goethe.

The celebrated German poet was then a man of sixty, highly educated and cultivated in all the arts. He had spent the greater part of his life in the service of the Duke of Weimar, and the luxury and etiquette of the court were an indispensable part of his existence.

It was a momentous occasion when the two men met, and each felt the significance of the moment. Beethoven had been so carried away by Goethe's marvelous poems that he longed to give the poet an equal inspiration through his music. He desired especially to make him realize how closely the two great arts, poetry and music, were related.

Goethe never forgot the first time he heard Beethoven play. The composer threw himself into the music until the muscles of his face swelled and the veins stood out. His eyes rolled wildly and seemed filled with an unearthly fire, and Goethe for the first time began to see that music could interpret the highest feelings of the human soul as well as poetry, if not better.

When Beethoven had finished playing he turned to Goethe expectantly, hoping that his efforts had reached the poet's heart.

But Goethe sat silent—transported. . . .

Beethoven looked at him for a moment with a puzzled

frown. Then a smile of understanding broke over his face. He went to him with his hand outstretched. "Ah, my friend!" he said with emotion, "is it because you are so moved that you sit silent?"

Goethe nodded, still unable to find words.

"Oh, sir, I didn't expect this from you!" Beethoven exclaimed. "I gave a concert in Berlin some years ago, and having done my best I was counting on considerable applause. But the audience sat silent, and I couldn't understand what was wrong." He smiled at the recollection. "Finally I discovered that the people of Berlin are so sensitive that instead of applauding they show their appreciation by waving their handkerchiefs wet with tears." His own eyes were moist. "I accept it gladly from you, my dear Goethe. When I read your poems they seem filled with music—I long to swing myself up to the same heights you had reached!"

"You have—you have!" cried Goethe with enthusiasm. "I have never heard so concentrated, so powerful, so intense an artist!" Beethoven had given him a new understanding of music.

As the days passed and the two men spent long hours together discussing and arguing over their opinions, they found one point on which they could not agree.

Goethe had a deep reverence for rank and aristocracy,

while Beethoven thought nothing of them. The musician could not understand why a man, simply because he happened to be born of a noble family, should be regarded as superior to one whom Nature has endowed with great gifts, such as the art of writing poetry or of creating beautiful music. Until Beethoven's time a musician—whether composer or performer—had been considered as hardly better than a servant—one who could be hired to furnish amusement for the members of the aristocracy. But already Beethoven's proud independence was creating a new respect for his craft, and the nobility were beginning to look up to and honor not only the musician but the art for which he stood.

Goethe, however, was anything but democratic in his ideas. Both by training and in character he belonged to the eighteenth century, and the traditions and customs of court life were deeply rooted in his nature.

One warm morning in July the two men started down the narrow streets of Teplitz together, so deep in their argument that they took no notice of the direction in which they were going.

"I tell you," Beethoven said with heat, "I have a contempt for all the nobility unless their superiority comes from within!" He smote his breast sharply as he walked along. "You can hang an order on a man, but that doesn't make him better in a single respect. You can *make* a court councilor or a privy chamberlain, but not," he added with a laugh, "a Goethe or a Beethoven!"

Goethe bit his lip in vexation. Such talk seemed to him in very poor taste. He was about to reply sharply that only a person *without* rank would be so ready to criticize its possession in others, when a company of the aristocracy who were summering at Teplitz came toward them. The Empress herself was among the group, and several of the Dukes and Archdukes. Goethe pulled his companion to one side of the road to let them pass, but Beethoven checked him imperiously.

"Keep hold of my arm," he exclaimed. "They must make way for us—not we for them!"

Goethe looked at him in horror. In those days, court etiquette was very strict and to violate its rules was an unheard-of thing. But Beethoven meant what he said, and finally Goethe released his companion's arm and stood to one side, hat off and head bared.

With arms folded, Beethoven walked through the royal group and only tilted his hat slightly. The Dukes stepped aside to make room for him and greeted him pleasantly.

When the company had passed, Beethoven stopped and waited for Goethe.

"You see," he said, "they respect me all the more because

I do not bow and scrape to them." He looked at Goethe with a disappointed air. "I waited for you because I honor and respect you as you deserve. Those others—" he nodded in the direction of the disappearing nobility—"what have they done that you should honor them so greatly?"

Goethe shook his head without replying. He felt that Beethoven was hopelessly lacking in proper feeling. The great musician seemed rough and ill-mannered to him. In a letter to a friend he wrote:

Karlsbad, September 2, 1812

. . . I made the acquaintance of Beethoven in Teplitz. His talent amazed me. However, he is unfortunately an utterly untamed person—not at all wrong if he finds the world detestable, but he does not thereby made it more enjoyable either for himself or for others. He is very much to be excused, on the other hand, and very much to be pitied, as his hearing is leaving him, which perhaps injures the musical part of his nature less than the social. By nature laconic, he becomes doubly so because of this lack.

Beethoven, on his side, felt a certain disappointment in Goethe. "The court atmosphere suits Goethe too well—better than it ought to suit such a poet," he wrote back to Vienna. It seemed to him that Goethe lacked the strong independence of spirit which the musician felt should be a vital part of all creative art.

The two men were so uncongenial both in personality and in education that they could never really understand each other. Yet, in spite of the difference between them, each recognized the genius of the other. Beethoven never ceased to admire Goethe, and though they never met again he was always proud to call the great poet his friend.

CHAPTER XVIII

"I AM THE BACCHUS . . ."

(1 8 1 2 - 1 5)

SUBMISSION, absolute submission to your fate," wrote Beethoven in his 1812 diary. "Thou mayest no longer be a man, not for thyself, only for others, for there is no longer happiness except in thyself, nothing must chain thee to life . . ."

For some time now, the master had been in wretched health. His hearing was steadily growing worse; soon, he realized, he would be completely deaf. But the words he had written as a young man of twenty-five, still remained his motto:

Courage! Despite all the weaknesses of the body, my
spirit shall rule!

Now, as if to prove that motto, he wrote a new symphony
so full of boisterous humor, so bubbling over with gay
vitality, that Richard Wagner called it "the apotheosis of
the dance," saying that it belonged "to the Night Spirit
and his crew, and if anyone plays it, tables and benches,
cans and cups, the grandmother, the blind and the lame,
aye, the children in the cradle, fall to dancing." *

Beethoven considered the Seventh Symphony one of his
greatest, though as usual when it was first heard there were
few people who really understood it. "He must be ready
for the mad-house!" said Carl Maria von Weber, whose
own *Invitation to the Dance* was later to be so popular.
Others alleged that Beethoven was intoxicated when he
wrote the work. "Yes," retorted Romain Rolland †— "he
was intoxicated—with poetry and genius."

"I am the Bacchus who presses out for men the delicious
nectar, and makes them spiritually drunk," Beethoven told
Bettina on that first memorable visit of theirs. "Music is

* This Symphony in A major has several times been presented in
choreographic form—that is, as a ballet: for instance, by the Ballet Russe
of Monte Carlo, and by Isadora Duncan, who in 1908 danced all move-
ments but the first at the Metropolitan Opera House, with full symphony
orchestra accompaniment.

† Author of *Jean Christophe,* that great biographical novel about a
musician which is founded, in part, on Beethoven's early years.

the wine that inspires one to new creation." The idea of a god who had the power to make men gay appealed strongly to him.* Through the intoxication of music it was possible, as he well knew, to escape from the troubles of everyday life.

Whatever the master's emotions—whether sorrow or joy, anger or love—they were always deep and passionate, and one extreme usually led to the other. He was forever alternating between the two, and his music as well as his temperament reflected this. When he was down in the depths, he had no sooner translated his depression into some composition full of somber tragedy than he rebounded in the opposite direction and wrote something gay or serene.

His symphonies were nearly all composed in pairs. Following the heroic Third came the lilting Fourth (sometimes called the "Spring" Symphony). Immediately after "Fate Knocks at the Door" (the Fifth) he wrote the serene and beautiful *Pastoral*. The great Seventh—that "shout of jubilation"—found its opposite in the Eighth, which Robert Haven Schauffler † calls the "Symphony Giocosa" . . . a "rich, sly, delicious compendium of purely musical wit, humor and buffoonery". . . whose Allegretto Scherzando

* After Beethoven's death, sketches were found for a Tenth Symphony, which was to have been dedicated to the god Bacchus.
† In *Beethoven, the Man Who Freed Music.*

"was destined to be the progenitor of the entire race of music devoted to elves, fays, nixies, trolls and fairies, from Weber to Mendelssohn to Ravel's *Mother Goose*." *

Beethoven's Seventh Symphony was not produced until some time after it was completed. At its first performance it was completely overshadowed by a far inferior work— one that roused tremendous enthusiasm because of its "timeliness" but is rarely heard today—the *Battle* Symphony or *Wellington's Victory*. Here is the way in which it came to be composed.

Shortly after he had finished the Seventh Symphony, Beethoven, one day, was passing by Herr Stein's piano manufactory in Vienna when he heard strange sounds issuing from within. Loud trumpets, drums, all manner of brass instruments—even to his deaf ears the noise was perceptible. He pushed open the door and went to the back of the shop.

"Herr Mälzel?" he inquired.

The music stopped abruptly. A thin, slightly stooped man looked up from the large, boxlike machine he had been working on. When he recognized Vienna's famous musician, he straightened up and hastily wiped his hands on the sides of his trousers.

* For the music of this Allegretto, see page 265.

"I understand you are a celebrated inventor," said Beethoven as he introduced himself. He looked with curiosity around the shop; anything mechanical always fascinated him. "Now what is this?" he inquired, picking up a small, clocklike object.

Mälzel smiled. "That should interest Your Excellency. For years the musicians have been trying to get me to make a machine that would mark time for them by clicking in whatever tempo they wish. It's nearly finished now. I call it a 'chronometer.'"

Beethoven was like a child with a new toy. "Why—it *works!*" he exclaimed in delight as Mälzel wound up the instrument and set it ticking.

"And this," Mälzel continued, pointing to another machine, "is my Mechanical Trumpeter. And here—" he opened up the case of the instrument he had been working on when the master came in—"is the gem of them all, the Panharmonicon."

Beethoven had heard about this famous invention. It was said to be the most ingenious musical mechanism ever designed. "All the instruments of a brass band are here represented." Mälzel demonstrated. "It makes a grand effect!" He showed Beethoven the revolving cylinders that reproduced the music—forerunner of the player-piano mechanism. "Already I have transcribed some fine pieces. Haydn's *Military* Symphony, for instance, is admirably suited to the Panharmonicon." He looked up hopefully, "Now if Herr van Beethoven felt inclined to compose a piece for the instrument . . . ?"

Beethoven, captivated by Mälzel's inventions, returned often to Herr Stein's piano factory to watch the completion of the Panharmonicon. The bellows that were used to blow the wind through the various brass instruments interested him especially.

"They also help to amplify the sound," Mälzel explained. As he said this, an idea occurred to him. Why wouldn't it be possible to invent some sort of amplifier for the human ear? He began experimenting, and a little later he presented Beethoven with a new invention of his—an ear-trumpet, which he called a "resonator." The composer was touchingly pleased. Though the instrument was a crude affair and ceased to be of much use to him as he grew progressively deafer, he kept it until he died, and it is still preserved in the Beethoven House in Bonn.

Mälzel planned to take his Panharmonicon to England. "It is sure to attract a great deal of attention there, and should make a lot of money," he told the master, "especially if we could announce a new composition by the celebrated Herr Ludwig van Beethoven! Something military in character, of course—suitable for the instrument's brass band; something that would appeal to the English temperament. . . ."

Beethoven had always greatly admired the English people. When, just at this time, the news reached Vienna of the Duke of Wellington's victory over the Napoleonic armies in Spain—the battle of Vitoria in the foot-hills of the Pyrenees—Beethoven decided that this would be a perfect subject for a composition; he could bring in "God Save the King" and "Malbrook" and "Rule, Britannia"— and plenty of drum rolls and trumpet flourishes!

Soon he was hard at work. At the top of the score he wrote:

> On Wellington's Victory at Vittoria, 1813, written
> for Herr Mälzel by Ludwig van Beethoven

Mälzel was delighted with the composition. He suggested that Beethoven arrange it for orchestra so that it could be played at concerts. Then they decided to give a grand charity benefit in Vienna. "We can start the program with my new symphony," said Beethoven.* "Then you can play some marches on your Mechanical Trumpeter with the orchestra accompanying."

"And *Wellington's Victory* will be the grand finale, of course," added Mälzel.

The composer planned to conduct the concert—though Mälzel didn't see how the unfortunate man could possibly

---

* The Seventh, then introduced for the first time.

direct an orchestra, since he would be able to hear only the loudest passages. Beethoven was worried, too. . . .

At the rehearsal he took his place before the musicians and rapped sharply with his baton. His face showed tense feeling as he began the opening passage of the symphony. In his anxiety to have the whole orchestra follow him, he threw his entire body into the effort. When the music was soft he gradually crouched down until he could hardly be seen by the musicians, and when a *forte* passage occurred he leapt into the air with arms outstretched.

Everyone began to smile at these queer antics. Then all at once Beethoven got ahead of the orchestra and began to gesticulate wildly for a *crescendo* while the players were still in the midst of a soft *piano* part. There were titters from the listeners, and the musicians were almost completely disrupted; they hardly knew where they were supposed to be playing.

Suddenly Beethoven discovered his error. In deep distress he peered anxiously around. Then, with a beckoning nod to Schuppanzigh to take his place, he left the conductor's platform precipitately and hurried out of the hall. Some time later Schuppanzigh found the master at home, stretched out on his couch and sleeping heavily. On his face was an expression of deep sadness, as if even in sleep he were conscious of his tragic fate.

In the spring of 1812, just before Mälzel was to go to England with his Panharmonicon (though actually the trip was postponed), Beethoven, Stephan von Breuning, Franz von Brunswick, and others gave a dinner in his honor. The master was in exceptionally high spirits that evening—well "unbuttoned," as he called it.

"A toast to the celebrated inventor of the Panharmonicon!" cried Stephan, raising his glass.

"Don't forget the 'chronometer,'" added Beethoven. "That's even more important—for us musicians, at least." He waved a mechanical beat: "Here's to Herr *Ta*-ta-*ta*-ta-*ta*-ta *Mäl*-zel!" Then he stopped short. "Why, that would make a good canon!" Quickly he jotted down a few lines and passed them around the table. And soon the whole group was singing lustily, in sharp, staccato imitation of the tick of Mälzel's chronometer: *"Ta*-ta-*ta*-ta-*ta*-ta *lie*-ber *Mäl*-zel!"

It happened that just at this time Beethoven was working on his Eighth Symphony, and the chronometer

Allegretto scherzando

1st Violins

Symphony No. 8, Allegretto

theme pleased him so much that he made use of it in the rollicking Allegretto movement of that work.*

Beethoven sighed deeply as he made a new entry in his diary. Another kitchenmaid discharged—another cook to be engaged! Life seemed one succession of incompetent servants. How he wished that he had someone to attend to the housekeeping for him, so that he might be freed of petty details!

A faint sound reached him as he sat at his writing table. He looked up inquiringly—someone was evidently knocking on the door, though to the unfortunate man the noise was only barely perceptible.

"Well, well, now, who is there?" he cried irascibly. A young boy opened the door with care. "I have a message from Herr Schuppanzigh," he announced timidly, holding out a letter.

Beethoven frowned. "Where is your tongue, boy?" he exclaimed, moving his hand about his ear as if he were groping for his sense of hearing.

---

* The symphony is Opus 93, in F major. Its Allegretto should not, however, be called the "metronome movement," as it commonly is; for Mälzel's *metronome* was not invented until 1816, and what Beethoven had in mind when he wrote the tick-tock movement of the Eighth in 1812 was the *chronometer*, Mälzel's earlier invention.

The youth repeated his words in a loud voice. The master listened attentively, and when he finally grasped the meaning of the words, the strained expression left his face, and he smiled with sudden good humor.

"Tell Herr Schuppanzigh that his message has been received and will be answered later," he said, looking more closely at the messenger. "What is your name, my boy?"

The youth came nearer with a beating heart. To him Beethoven represented everything that was noblest and highest in life, and when he had been bidden to deliver a letter to the great composer he could hardly believe in his good fortune.

"My name is Anton Schindler, sir," he shouted into the deaf man's ear.

Beethoven nodded kindly and asked him where he lived. Then he began to grumble under his breath. "Fancy my predicament. Here you find your celebrated Beethoven under house arrest!"

Schindler said he hoped the master was not ill. "Ill?" Beethoven complained. "I am always ill. But this time," he exclaimed with a chuckle, "it's my boots that are ill." He looked at the boy a little defiantly. "You see, I have only one pair, and when they need mending . . . !" He waved his hand as if dismissing the subject.

Schindler, sadly impressed by the master's condition, wished that there were some way in which he could be of service to him. It was a wish that found rare fulfillment in later years—as sincere wishes often have a way of doing. Anton Schindler came to be the master's chief support during the last part of his life, and he was the first to write a Beethoven biography.

A short time later, Beethoven's brother Carl died after an illness of several months, and Ludwig was left the chief executor of his estate. Sitting in the stuffy little dining-room of his brother's house, he read the will aloud to his sister-in-law and the wide-eyed boy who clung to her skirts. Little Karl was his brother's only child, and because he had grown so devoted to the boy Beethoven had almost forgiven Carl's unfortunate marriage—though he still disapproved violently of his sister-in-law.

He adjusted his thick spectacles and cleared his throat:

Vienna, Nov. 17, 1815

Certain that all men must die and feeling that I am near this goal, but in full possession of my understanding, I freely and voluntarily make these my last dispositions. . . . I appoint my brother Ludwig van Beethoven guardian (to my son Karl). Inasmuch as my deeply beloved brother has often aided me with true brotherly love in the most magnanimous manner, I ask, in full confidence and trust in his noble heart, that he shall bestow the love and friendship he often showed me, upon my son Karl, and do all that is possible to promote the intellectual training and further welfare of my son. I know that he will not deny me this my request.

Beethoven's eyes filled with tears as he read this tribute. In spite of the many wrongs his brother had done him during his lifetime, Beethoven had never ceased to love him. Little Karl would be like his own son. Beethoven was ready to sacrifice everything for him and devote his life to the child if necessary.

The scornful voice of his sister-in-law broke in on his reflections.

"What was Carl thinking of to make *you* guardian of my child!" The widow looked at her husband's brother with open hostility. "A man who can't even keep his own affairs in order!" she added under her breath.

Beethoven's eyes flashed. The woman's character had not improved with the passing years. What would become of the child if he were left to her influence?

Although Carl had added a codicil to his will, stating that he did not wish the son to be taken away from his mother, Beethoven could not bear the thought of leaving his nephew with a woman of whom he disapproved so intensely.

"The boy will immediately be sent to a private school," he said. "I know the very place for him."

Frau van Beethoven tossed her head defiantly. "We shall see about that!" she answered with quiet fury.

When Stephan von Breuning heard of Carl's will, he hurried over to remonstrate with Beethoven. "Leave the boy to his mother!" he pleaded. "Otherwise she will be sure to make trouble for you; and you don't know how he will turn out even if you are able to separate him from her and bring him up yourself."

Beethoven was indignant. "Would you have me desert my own flesh and blood?" he demanded. "Refuse the dying request of my brother? No, I am not so base as that!"

Breuning saw that it would be useless to argue with him.

"Some day you will regret it!" he said with conviction. "However, if you should need help," he went on, placing his hand affectionately on Beethoven's shoulder, "be sure to let me know."

But the master was stubbornly determined to manage his own affairs, and he was rather glad that Stephan was leaving Vienna to make his home in another city.

During the years that followed, Beethoven regretted more than once that he had not taken Stephan's advice. He found himself constantly involved in lawsuits with his sister-in-law over the guardianship of Karl. Though incessantly harassed and tormented, he obstinately refused to allow anyone else to help him in managing the boy. In his desire to fulfill his brother's dying request, and his own deep love for his nephew, he didn't stop to consider how ill-fitted he was for the upbringing of a young boy.

The disorder of his home life, his own violent temperament and irregular habits, provided a far from favorable environment for an impressionable child. And in his management of the boy Beethoven was no wiser. He would alternate between unnecessarily stern discipline and such wild indulgence as would have spoiled even a child with a naturally fine character.

And Karl did not have a naturally fine character. He was sly, lazy, and shiftless. As the years went by he resented his uncle's discipline more and more, and there were constant disputes between the two. Beethoven could not tolerate the slightest dishonesty, and his nephew's loose ways distressed him beyond measure.

Karl was incessantly begging for money, and when his uncle would not give it to him he would borrow it from anyone who was willing to lend it. Beethoven was always furious when he learned of it.

"Last Sunday you again borrowed a florin fifteen kreutzer from the kitchen wench!" he exclaimed one day, looking at his nephew with flashing eyes. "This was forbidden. And it is just the same in everything!"

Then Karl would sulk and even threaten to kill himself, and his uncle would immediately repent his harshness and forgive him again.

There were endless quarrels and separations, continued reconciliations and promises for the future. But Karl, in spite of all admonitions, continued on his wayward path.

After the departure of Stephan von Breuning and Ries from Vienna, Beethoven turned frequently to Anton Schindler for help and advice. The younger man's desire to be of service to the master had brought him very close to the great musician, and he devoted himself unselfishly to Beethoven's interests. He helped him with his accounts, shielded him from the prying curiosity of idle people, and gradually came to take the position that should have been held by the composer's own nephew Karl.

Now for the first time in his life, Beethoven found it difficult to write music. The anxiety over Karl and the petty details of everyday life served—for the time, at least —to dry up the fountainhead of his inspiration. The next few years were the least productive of his entire career.

But finally in 1818, like a stream that had been too long checked, the spring of inspiration began once more to flow.

CHAPTER XIX

HYMN TO JOY

(1818-24)

I S IT HERR VAN BEETHOVEN that you're looking for?"
called a voice from a neighboring house. "Oh, the poor
man—he has surely lost his mind!"

Anton Schindler raised his head in surprise. He and a
friend had just driven out to Mödling to see the master.
What on earth could have happened?

"Both of the great man's servants left this morning," the neighbor continued. "There was a fearful row at midnight! It seems he was so busy writing music that he forgot his dinner. The servants got tired of waiting—you can hardly blame them for that—and they both fell asleep. When Herr van Beethoven finally remembered his dinner, it was completely spoiled. And there was the devil to pay!"

Schindler looked grave. He knew only too well how unreasonable the master was when exhausted by long hours of labor. No doubt he was working on the wonderful new *Missa Solemnis* for the Archduke Rudolph.

Rudolph, youngest son of the Emperor Leopold II, had long been Beethoven's good friend and patron. The composer had dedicated to this royal friend and pupil a considerable number of important works, including the opera *Fidelio,* the Fourth and the Fifth (*Emperor*) concertos, the sonatas called *Adieu, Absence, and Reunion,* and *Hammerklavier,* and the *Archduke* Trio, Opus 97. When, in 1818, Beethoven heard that Rudolph was to be made Archbishop of Olmütz, he decided to write a solemn Mass for the consecration ceremonies and, moving out to Mödling, he started to work.

As Schindler and his friend reached the door of the house in which Beethoven was staying, they heard a great singing, howling, and stamping within. There was no answer to their loudest knocks; either Beethoven failed to hear them, or he didn't want to be disturbed. For some time they stood outside the door, trying to decide whether it would be better to break it down and rescue the unfortunate man, or to wait until he came to his senses. Then suddenly the door opened and the master himself confronted the two visitors.

He was only half-dressed, and he had evidently not shaved for some days. His eyes were wild and his whole appearance gave the effect of one who had been battling with unseen powers. At first his words were confused, but gradually he became more coherent.

"Pretty doings, these!" he exclaimed wrathfully. "Everybody has run away, and I haven't had a thing to eat since yesterday noon."

Schindler tried to calm him, and—while his companion went to a neighboring eating house to order food for the famished man—he helped Beethoven to dress and make himself presentable. The master never cared what he wore or how he looked. When his old clothes got too disreputable, Schindler would replace them with new, and Beethoven never even noticed the change.

"I have just received a wonderful gift," he said, when he was finally restored to his normal state. "Those English people, how genuine they are—what hearts of gold!" And he showed them a splendid new mahogany piano that had been sent to him from London by Thomas Broadwood, the celebrated piano manufacturer, pointing with pride to the name inlaid in letters of ebony:

BEETHOVEN

He ran his fingers lightly over the keys. "With the help of Mälzel's resonator I can even hear the tone! Such a fine pianoforte!" He shook his head reminiscently. "When I was a boy in Bonn, I used to dream of a piano like this."

He played for them a few passages from the new *Missa Solemnis*. But the two men were unable to appreciate the music. "You should have the instrument tuned," Schindler said, wincing.

Beethoven shook his head. He was so afraid that something might happen to his precious piano that he wouldn't allow anyone to touch it. It made no difference to *him* if it was out of tune—he couldn't hear it. . . .

While he was working on the *Missa Solemnis* he became so preoccupied with composition, so lost to the world, that he grew even more absent-minded than usual. Once he went to a tavern, forgot to order a meal, and then insisted on paying for it. Another time, after sitting for about an hour staring into space, he called the waiter. "How much is my bill?" he asked. "But the gentleman hasn't eaten anything yet," said the waiter in surprise. "What shall I bring?" Beethoven looked at him in bewilderment. "Bring anything you please," he answered shortly; "only in heaven's name leave me alone!"

One morning, intent on his thoughts, he left the house without either hat or coat. All day he tramped through the country, unconscious of time or direction. Toward evening, as he reached the outskirts of a small town, he felt a rough hand on his shoulder.

"Where do you think you are going, my fine fellow?" asked a peremptory voice. Beethoven, frowning, looked up to see a policeman standing over him.

"Better come along to the jail with me," the man continued. "We don't want tramps around here."

"*Tramps!*" Beethoven drew himself up to his full five feet, three inches. "You *Dumkopf!* Don't you know that I am Beethoven, the composer?"

But the officer only laughed. "Yes, you *look* like a great composer—no hat, no coat . . . Come along now."

The master was not one to allow himself to be unjustly treated. He demanded that the Burgomaster be called. When this was refused, he set up such a racket that finally, in the middle of the night, the Burgomaster was summoned, and at last Beethoven was identified and freed—with the town's apologies.

"Sacrifice again all the pettiness of social life to your art," he wrote in his diary that summer at Mödling. "O God above all things! For it is an eternal providence which directs omnisciently the good and evil fortunes of human man. . . . Tranquilly will I submit myself to all vicissitudes and place my sole confidence in Thy unalterable goodness, O God! My soul shall rejoice. . . . Be my rock, my light, forever my trust!"

Beethoven rarely attended church, and because of his natural independence he was intolerant of outward ritual. Yet at heart he was deeply religious. When the idea of the *Missa Solemnis* came to him, it took the form of the conventional church Mass, but at the same time it was a medium for the expression of his own deep devotion.

At the top of the score he wrote:

From the heart—may it speak to the heart.

For nearly five years Beethoven worked on the *Missa*. By the time it was completed in 1822, the Archduke Rudolph had long since been consecrated Bishop of Olmütz, and the work was not heard until 1824.

A revival of the opera *Fidelio* was planned for November 1822, and Beethoven, against everybody's advice, was determined to conduct.

"Do you think it wise, master?" protested Schindler. "Wouldn't it be better if Umlauf directed the performance?"

"Umlauf can assist," Beethoven answered shortly.

At the dress rehearsal he took his place at the conductor's stand with Umlauf beside him. The orchestra had been well rehearsed in the overture, so that this went off in fine form, and the master looked towards Schindler with a "You see . . . !" air. But when the singing began, it became evident that he could not hear the voices, and soon all was confusion.

Umlauf motioned for the performance to stop. They began again. The same thing happened. "Neither the director nor Umlauf was willing to speak the saddening words: 'It will not do; go away, you unhappy man!'" wrote Schindler in telling of the incident.

Beethoven looked around in consternation. Anxiously he scrutinized the faces to discover the reason for the interruption. But everywhere there was silence. Finally he fumbled for his Conversation Book and handed it to Schindler.

"Please do not go on," Schindler wrote in it. "More at home."

Beethoven took the hint. "With a bound he was in the parterre and said merely: 'Out, quick!' Without stopping he ran toward his lodgings. Inside he threw himself on the sofa, covered his face with his hands and remained in this attitude till we sat down to eat. During the meal not a word came from his lips; he was a picture of profound melancholy and depression. . . ."

"In all seriousness," wrote Friedrich Rochlitz in 1822 of Beethoven, "he seems amiable, or, if this word startles you, I say: The gloomy, unlicked bear is so winning and confiding, growls and shakes his hairy coat so harmlessly and curiously, that it is delightful, and one could not help liking him even if he were but a bear and had done nothing but what a bear can do."

Rochlitz, coming to Vienna from Leipzig, had made the acquaintance of the "gruff bear"—as Beethoven had

been described to him. At one of their visits the talk turned
to Goethe.

"Why don't you compose some music for Goethe's
Faust?" asked Rochlitz. "Something on the order of your
great *Egmont.*"

"Ha!" cried Beethoven, throwing his hands into the air.
"That *would* be a piece of work!" He stared up at the
ceiling. "Something might come of it. . . ." He began to
outline a plan for the work; then he stopped and was silent
for a moment. "First, though, I have other compositions
that must be finished. For quite a while now I've been
occupied with three big works—two symphonies and an
oratorio. A good part of them is already hatched out—in
my head, that is." An apprehensive look came into his
eyes. "These works will take a long time. . . . You see,
for some time I haven't been able to bring myself to write
easily. I sit and think and think. The ideas are there, but
they won't go down on paper. I dread the beginning of
any large work—though, once begun, it goes all right."

The "oratorio" was the *Missa Solemnis,* and the "two
symphonies" later resolved themselves into one—the last
that Beethoven was to write, and the greatest.

Already in 1818, while beginning the *Missa,* the idea
for this "two in one" symphony had presented itself. In
his notebook—that reservoir from which he drew his
material—he wrote:

Adagio Cantique.

Pious song in a symphony in the ancient modes—Lord God we praise Thee—alleluia— The whole 2d sinfonie might be characterized in this manner, in which case the vocal parts would enter in the last movement or already in the Adagio.

Shut off from the world, poor, broken in health and now almost totally deaf, Beethoven planned this new work as a mighty hymn of praise and thanksgiving, an expression of the highest joy of which man is capable—that joy which comes from within. This great Ninth Symphony—from the majestic opening through the Scherzo, which he said flashed into his mind like a sudden outburst of light after long darkness; and the Andante, like a holy communion of the soul; to the final triumphant outburst of joy—remains one of the world's great wonders.

Beethoven worked at it, altogether, for six years. But when it was completed he hesitated to have it performed. He had lost faith in the Viennese. Their taste in music seemed to him to have deteriorated. Rossini, the Italian composer, was all the rage at that time. Beethoven had no very high regard for Rossini's music; he called him "a good scene-painter." "He would have been great if only his teacher had frequently applied some blows to his posterior." The master felt that the people of Vienna preferred Rossini's music to his own. "His music suits the frivolous and sensuous spirit of the times; and," he added, remembering his lifelong labors over *Fidelio,* "his productivity is so great that he needs only as many weeks as the Germans need years to write an opera."

The master still had many loyal friends, however. One day Schindler found Beethoven standing by the window with a scroll in his hand. He seemed very much moved.

"Read it," he said briefly, handing the paper to Schindler. It was a petition signed by thirty of the master's friends and admirers.

To Herr Ludwig van Beethoven:

Out of the wide circle of reverent admirers surrounding your genius in this your second native city, there approach you today a small number of the disciples and lovers of art to give expression to long-felt wishes, timidly to prefer a long-suppressed request. . . .

Do not withhold longer from the popular enjoyment, do not keep longer from the oppressed sense of that which is great and perfect, a performance of the latest masterworks of your hand. We know that a new flower glows in the garland of your glorious, still unequaled symphonies. . . . For years . . . we have waited and hoped to see you distribute new gifts from the fulness of your riches to the circle of your friends. Do not longer disappoint the general expectations! . . . Appear soon among your friends, your admirers, your venerators! . . . This is your nearest and first prayer.

Need we tell you with what regret your retirement from public life has filled us? . . . You alone are able to insure a decisive victory to the efforts of the best amongst us. From you the native Art Society and the German Opera expect new blossoms, rejuvenated life and a new sovereignty of the true and beautiful over the dominion to which the prevalent spirit of fashion wishes to subject even the eternal laws of art. Bid us hope that the wishes of all who have listened to the sound of your harmonies will soon be fulfilled! This is our most urgent second prayer. . . .

May the year which we have begun not come to an end without rejoicing us with the fruits of our petition and may the coming spring when it witnesses the unfolding of one of our longed-for gifts become a twofold blooming-time for us and for all the world of art!

Vienna, February 1824

While Schindler was reading the long document, Beethoven stood silent, gazing out of the window. Then he turned and said with emotion: "Beautiful, isn't it! It rejoices me greatly."

Recently he had been in a very despondent mood, and had grown more and more suspicious of the people around him, feeling that everyone was against him. The "petition" helped to restore his confidence, and finally he agreed to his friends' request.

But the concert was some time in materializing. The master proved temperamental and uncertain—it was impossible to pin him down to a date. Finally Count Moritz

Lichnowsky, Schuppanzigh, and Schindler resorted to a ruse to make him sign an agreement. After they left him, he saw through the trick and flew into a temper. To each of the three went a peremptory note:

To Count Moritz: *"I despise treachery. Do not visit me again. No concert."*

To Schuppanzigh: *"Let him not visit me more. I shall give no concert."*

To Schindler: *"I request you not to come again until I send for you. No concert."*

Beethoven never hesitated to express himself, either orally or in writing. Once when a music-copyist presumed to send him a note objecting to certain of the master's criticisms, Beethoven returned the letter to him. Scrawled across the writing in two-inch letters was:

STUPID, CONCEITED, ASININE FELLOW

while on the reverse of the sheet he wrote:

BOTCHING-SCRIBBLER!

STUPID FELLOW!

Correct the blunders you have made in your ignorance, insolence, conceit, and stupidity—this would be more to the purpose than to try to teach me, which is as if a *Sow* were to try to give lessons to *Minerva!*

Not content with this, in the margin he added: "Do you do honor to Mozart and Haydn by never mentioning their names," and "I decided yesterday and even before then *not to have you write any more* for me."

At long last the concert that Beethoven's friends had been praying for materialized. Early in May an official announcement appeared in the newspapers:

GRAND MUSICAL CONCERT
By Herr L. van Beethoven
TOMORROW, MAY 7, 1824
In the R. I. Court Theater beside the Kärnthnerthor
The musical pieces to be performed are
the latest works of Herr Ludwig van Beethoven
First: A Grand Overture *
Second: Three Grand Hymns with Solo and
Chorus Voices †
Third: A Grand Symphony with Solo and
Chorus Voices entering in the finale
on Schiller's Ode to Joy

Herr Schuppanzigh has undertaken the direction of the orchestra. Herr Ludwig van Beethoven himself will participate in the general direction.

When the rehearsals for the concert started, trouble also started. Beethoven, with his usual disregard of vocal limitations, had written the choral parts in such a high register that the singers could scarcely reach the upper

---

* *The Consecration of the House.* † From the *Missa Solemnis.*

notes. Fräulein Unger, one of the soloists, asked the master if he wouldn't change the passages. She might as well have saved her breath. "Singers should be able to do anything," he once remarked, and added with a grin, "except, perhaps, bite their own noses."

Fräulein Unger was so incensed that she called Beethoven—to his face, but fortunately he couldn't hear her—a "tyrant over all the vocal organs." "Evidently we'll have to go on torturing ourselves—in the name of God!" she told her fellow soloist, Frau Sontag. "But as to those highest notes—we simply won't sing them. If we open our mouths wide enough, Beethoven won't know the difference."

Ludwig van Beethoven's Ninth Symphony was a daring experiment. Once before, in 1818, he had written a *Fantasia* for pianoforte, orchestra, and chorus (Opus 80), but no one had ever heard of putting singers in a *symphony!* When the master decided to use the poet Schiller's *Ode to Joy* in the last movement, he felt that only a mighty combination of both orchestra and the human voice could do justice to the theme. It was while he was still in Bonn (perhaps at one of those evenings at Frau von Breuning's, when the classics were read aloud) that he first came across Schiller's great work. The musical theme for the *Ode to Joy* had also occurred to him earlier. He used it in a song written in 1805, called prophetically "To Hope" (*An die Hoffnung,* Opus 32).

Allegro assai

Symphony No. 9, Choral, finale ("Ode to Joy")

Beethoven was to conduct the overture at the "Grand Concert." Schindler tactfully suggested: "It would put too severe a strain on your ears to conduct the whole concert. You can indicate the proper tempo at the beginning of each piece." The performers were instructed to pay no attention to the deaf master's beat, but to follow the music in their scores.

At the final rehearsal, Beethoven was "dissolved in devotion and emotion." He could not hear the outer sounds, but the music was clear to his inner consciousness, and it moved him profoundly. When the rehearsal was ended, he stood at the door and embraced each of the performers as they went out.

All of the master's old friends came, on that memorable evening of May 7, 1824. Even the aged Baron Zmeskall— now a bedridden invalid—insisted on being carried to the hall in a sedan-chair. The theater was completely filled, with one notable exception. The royal box stood empty. Only a few days before, Beethoven—accompanied by Schindler—had gone to call on the Imperial family with his personal invitation to attend. But not one of them came. . . .

On the night of the concert Schindler went over to help Beethoven get ready. "But, master," he exclaimed in dismay, "surely you are not going to wear that old green coat?"

Beethoven shrugged his shoulders. "I don't own a decent black one," he said regretfully. "But the theater will be dark, and no one will notice."

The "Grand Concert" proved the greatest, and the last, of the master's triumphs. During the playing of the Ninth Symphony the audience became so enthusiastic that everyone kept breaking in with applause. At the end of the Scherzo, Beethoven stood looking through the pages of his score, apparently oblivious to the clapping. Fräulein Unger touched him on the sleeve.

"Look—" she murmured, her eyes full of tears. Gently she turned the deaf man around so that he could *see* the applause and the wildly cheering audience.

After the concert Beethoven invited Schindler, Schuppanzigh, and another friend to have dinner with him at the "Zum Wilden Mann" restaurant on the Prater. Schindler wished to report on the concert's success, and— since it was now impossible to communicate with the unfortunate musician except in writing—the report was written in the Conversation Book as the four sat waiting to be served.

"Never in my life," wrote Schindler as Beethoven watched the lines of writing, "did I hear such frenetic yet cordial applause. Once the second movement of the symphony was completely stopped by applause—and there was a demand for an encore. The reception was more than imperial, for the people burst out in a storm four times. At the last there were cries of *Vivat!* . . . When the parterre broke out in applauding cries the fifth time, the Police Commissioner yelled *'Silence!'* "

"How about the receipts?" Beethoven asked.

Schindler hesitated. "The expenses were very heavy, you know. The large chorus, and the soloists—and an orchestra nearly twice as large as usual."

Beethoven's eyes began to flash. "How much was left over?" he demanded ominously.

"Well—they took in twenty-two hundred florins."

"Yes?"

"And after the expenses were paid four hundred and twenty florins were left."

Then Beethoven exploded. Everything about the concert, he charged, had been mismanaged. There was a conspiracy against him. He had been cheated. . . . Violently his temper mounted. The "Wild Man Restaurant" had never seen a wilder man. But the three friends didn't wait for the final outburst. They knew their master's temper too well. Hurriedly they reached for their hats and beat a hasty retreat.

Just then the waiter arrived with dinner for four. Beethoven ate his meal in solitary grandeur. . . .

CHAPTER XX

STEPHAN RETURNS

(1 8 2 6)

STEPHAN VON BREUNING, recently returned to Vienna,
was walking one afternoon in 1826 with his young
son Gerhard along the ramparts—the famous walk
on the top of the old walls surrounding the city. These
ancient fortifications were torn down in 1858 and converted
into one of the most beautiful avenues in the world—the

292

celebrated Ringstrasse. But in Beethoven's day the old walls were still standing, and one of the master's favorite walks was along these ramparts.

Coming from the opposite direction Breuning and Gerhard noticed a solitary figure, bent but still powerful, stalking energetically toward them. He wore an old, dilapidated felt hat pushed well back on his massive forehead, with shaggy locks of gray hair escaping from beneath. The loose ends of a shabby scarf streamed away from his broad turned-down collar, and the coattails of a worn blue suit with tarnished brass buttons flapped heavily about his legs. A watch hung neglected by his side—fortunately well moored to its owner by a stout chain—and his pockets bulged with notebooks, pencils, and even a cumbersome ear-trumpet. As he walked, the man grumbled to himself and occasionally waved his arms about his head.

A number of street gamins began to collect behind him. Before long they were imitating his gestures, and finally, unable to attract his attention, they circled around him and began to shout: *"Verrückter!—crazy one!"*

Suddenly Stephan von Breuning stopped short with a cry of astonishment.

"As I live, Gerhard," he exclaimed. "It's *Beethoven!*"

At that moment the master looked up, and when he recognized his old friend he fell upon him joyfully.

"Well, well, Stephan, what luck, what happiness!" he

cried as he embraced him affectionately. "When did you return to Vienna? Where have you been keeping yourself?"

Stephan was delighted at the encounter. "Rather, I should say, where have *you* been keeping yourself, Ludwig? For days I have been trying to find you! I learn your address from someone, and behold when I seek you there, you have gone—with no trace left!"

Beethoven waved his hand sharply and pulled out his ear-trumpet. "You were saying . . . ?"

Breuning repeated his remarks in a loud voice into the trumpet.

The master shook his head sadly. "It's no use, Stephan —I cannot hear." He reached into the voluminous pockets of his coattails and drew out his Conversation Book and a thick carpenter's pencil. "You will have to write it down."

Stephan gazed at him sympathetically.

"What a fine boy you have!" Beethoven exclaimed as they walked along. "A regular 'trousers-button' of a fellow!" He looked closely at Gerhard through his thick spectacles. "There is something about him, yes—he is like Lorchen!"

The gamins still persisted in running after them. Beethoven noticed it at last.

"I don't know why they always follow me," he complained. "Karl, now—he will no longer be seen on the streets with me." He looked at Stephan wistfully. "Only yesterday he said: 'The people make merry at your expense because you have such a bad hat!' My own nephew—after all I have done for him, to be ashamed of me . . ." His face set in a grim scowl.

Gerhard pulled at his father's sleeve. "I think it an honor to walk with such a great man, don't you, Father?"

"If only I had taken your advice when my brother died, Stephan, and let someone else have the guardianship of that worthless boy!" Beethoven sighed heavily. "It has brought me only sorrow."

"Come home with us for dinner, and we will talk it over," Breuning wrote in the book.

As Beethoven noticed the direction which they were taking, he exclaimed with pleasure: "Is this your neighborhood? What luck! I am just about to move into the Schwarzspanierhaus, and you—I do declare," as they turned into Breuning's residence, "directly across—this *is* fortunate!"

Stephan, who had married and acquired a family since he left Vienna, was eager to present his wife and children to Beethoven. The master, in his joy at finding his old friend again, was full of high spirits and admired everything. He looked carefully around the neat and comfortable home and sighed dismally as he remembered his own disordered lodgings.

"Ah, Stephan," he said with deep feeling, "you are more

fortunate than you realize. Beautiful children, an attractive home, a charming wife to look after it. While I," he continued gloomily, "I cannot even find a servant who will take proper care of my things. No one to brush my clothes—put my poor possessions in order. If it were not for young Schindler I don't know how I should exist!"

Frau von Breuning was filled with pity for the unfortunate man. She noticed how wretchedly ill-kept his clothes were, and yet how snow-white the linen that he wore. She seized his Conversation Book and wrote rapidly on one of the pages: "Let me help you. Since we are to be such near neighbors it will be no trouble at all for me to slip over occasionally and see that your things are looked after."

Beethoven looked at her in grateful surprise. "How kind of you!" Of late years so many had taken advantage of his unfortunate condition that he knew how to appreciate a helpful spirit. He went over to the window and looked down at the street below.

Gerhard whispered to his father: "Do you think he would play for us?"

Stephan shook his head. "They say he never plays for anyone now. But I should like to have him hear you," he added, forgetting his friend's infirmity.

Gerhard seated himself at the piano and began to play softly. The master paid no attention. The boy grew bolder and finally played with all his strength.

Beethoven left the window and looked surprised when he saw Gerhard at the piano—not a sound had reached him. He came over and watched him for a few moments. "Another prodigy?" he laughed. Gerhard stopped in confusion and shook his head in violent denial. The master pulled his ear gently. "Ah, well, perhaps not a genius like young Franz Liszt, but you have talent there, I can see it."

He let his hand fall heavily on the piano. Gerhard looked up with eager anticipation, but Beethoven only laughed and walked away.

"You thought I was going to play for you, didn't you?" His expression changed to sadness. "What is the use of playing when one can no longer hear the tones?"

Beethoven once showed his fine Broadwood piano to a friend named Rellstab. "Only see what a beautiful tone it has!" the musician said, and without taking his eyes from Rellstab's face, he put his hands on the keys and gently struck a chord. "Never will any chord enter my soul so poignant, so heartbreaking as that one was!" said Rellstab in telling of this visit. "He struck the C major triad with his right hand, struck B in the bass with his left, and, continuing to gaze uninterruptedly at me, repeated the false chord several times in order to let the sweet tone of the instrument reverberate; and the greatest musician on earth did not hear the dissonance!"

When they sat down to dinner that day at the Breunings', the master looked with pleasure at the smiling faces around the table. He was especially pleased when he found that the main course was his favorite fish.

"And yet," he said, as if to excuse his interest in the food, "we mustn't think too much about what we eat! Man is but little above the animals if he finds his chief satisfaction at the dinner table!"

Gerhard, who was treasuring every word of the master, thought that here surely was a man who had passed beyond the bonds of physical existence.

Suddenly the smallest child—she was named after her aunt Lorchen—gave a piercing shriek.

Beethoven turned in startled surprise. He had heard the sound! he had actually heard it! . . . What happiness to find that there was still something that he could hear! He laughed joyously, and Gerhard noticed what fine straight white teeth he had.

He even spoke of his deafness, a subject that was usually too painful for him to discuss.

"Your brother-in-law Wegeler thinks my trouble comes

from too much bathing," he said to Stephan with a laugh. "But I couldn't live without my baths! When I am in the midst of composing, often the only thing that helps my thoughts is to pour water over my head. Perhaps I haven't been careful enough about going out afterward into the wet and cold with these shaggy locks—" he ran his fingers through his thick gray hair—"half dripping still. But it's not the water that does the harm—" Beethoven shook his head in discouragement—"it's the intestinal trouble."

Stephan and his wife exchanged sympathetic glances.

"Always in the winter I am ill," the master went on mournfully. "Then in the summer, when I can get away to the country, my health seems to come back." He was silent a moment. "But Karl, now—he doesn't like the country." He sighed again and looked at Stephan as if for advice. "I don't know what to do with the boy. It's always debts with him—always troubles!"

"What are you writing now, Ludwig?" Stephan asked to change the subject.

Beethoven's eyes lit up. "The best of all!"

Stephan laughed. "I suppose an artist always thinks that whatever he is working on at the moment is 'the best.' But, you know, nothing could be greater than your wonderful Ninth Symphony!"

The master shook his head slightly. "A symphony is

grand; it makes a big effect. But the finest music of all is that written for only a few instruments. Two years ago Prince Galitzin asked me to compose three quartets for him. What joy they have brought me! And—" he added with childlike satisfaction—"it's the best music I ever wrote."

Beethoven's last five string quartets and the Great Fugue—the concluding work of his life—are often considered to be the greatest music ever composed. Even today these works are not easy for the average concert-goer to understand; only after study and frequent hearing can one begin to appreciate their depth and matchless beauty.

Perhaps because the writing of these quartets brought him so much joy, Beethoven called the first of the group (in E flat, Opus 127) "La Gaieté." But it sings not of youth's feverish gaiety, but of the mellow contentment of a man who has lived through the passions of life and is finally able to look back and see that it was good.

The second—the A Minor Quartet, Opus 132—was written in the spring of 1825. Beethoven had been ill again, and while he was recovering he sketched out this quartet. In his notebook he called it a "Hymn of Thanksgiving to God of an invalid on his convalescence. . . . Feeling a new strength and reawakened feeling."

The quartet in B flat (Opus 130), which followed next, was perhaps Beethoven's favorite; to the end of his life he confessed that when he recalled the *Cavatina* (the fifth movement), he was moved to tears.

Quartet in B flat, Opus 130, Cavatina

"Surely this quartet is the greatest of them all, isn't it, master?" asked Holz, a young disciple who came into Beethoven's life during these last years.

The composer would not commit himself. "Each in its

way!" he answered with a shrug. "Art demands of us not to stand still. You will find there a new way of voice-leading [part-writing]." Then he added, with characteristic detachment, "And, thank God, there is less lack of fancy than ever before."

As originally composed, the last movement of this B-flat quartet, in fugue form, was so long and difficult to understand that Beethoven was finally persuaded to substitute another finale; and the fugue itself was published separately as Opus 133, the "Great Fugue."

When the score of the C-sharp Minor Quartet (Opus 131) was turned over to Schott & Sons, music publishers, they sent back an indignant letter. "You promised us an entirely new work," they said. "But on the manuscript is written: 'Put together from one thing and another.'"

Beethoven laughed heartily when he read the letter. "That was only a joke," he wrote back. "Don't worry— the quartet is brand-new."

"Brand-new" (*funkelnagelneu*) was a conservative way of describing what was perhaps the master's greatest work —the perfect flowering of a life of masterpieces—and, after the Great Fugue, the most difficult to understand. Beethoven himself felt that it was his best; and Wagner called the Scherzo of this quartet the "chef d'œuvre of all music." The middle movement is made up of an unforgettable Andante theme and variations.

Andante, ma non troppo e molto cantabile

*Quartet in C sharp minor, Opus 131, middle movement,
theme and variations*

After Stephan's return, Beethoven frequently visited the Breuning household. One day while he was there, late that summer of 1826, a roughly dressed cart driver came to the door.

"A messenger for you, Ludwig," Stephan cried. Beethoven rose stiffly and went outside while Breuning returned to the living-room.

Presently a loud groan reached the ears of the family. Stephan and his wife rushed to the door and found Beethoven leaning against the wall. He could scarcely speak.

"Do you know what has happened?" he exclaimed feebly. "My Karl—my Karl—" his voice shook—"he has shot himself."

Stephan gave an exclamation of pity and put his arm about the man's shaking shoulders. Frau von Breuning wrung her hands. "He is not—*dead?*"

"No, thank God. He only grazed himself with the bullet. But how he has disgraced me! And I love him so very dearly! . . . Is it true, Stephan, that they can arrest Karl for this?"

Breuning nodded; for under Austrian law a person who attempted suicide was guilty of a crime.

"Oh, my poor boy, my poor boy!" Beethoven groaned.

Stephan went with him to the hospital, where Karl had been put in the three-florin ward.

"How *could* you . . . ?" he exclaimed brokenly.

But his nephew only muttered, "Don't plague me with reproaches," and turned his face to the wall.

As it turned out, Karl was not seriously wounded, and it was thought that he would soon recover. Schindler went over on the following day to interview the boy and try to find out the reason for his act.

"When I spoke to him of you he said, 'If only he would not show himself again . . . I am tired of his reproaches!'" Schindler reported to the master.

Beethoven groaned loudly and dropped his great head in his hands. His shoulders were bowed with grief, and he looked two decades older than his fifty-six years.

"He even threatened to tear the bandages off if anything more were said to him about his uncle!" Schindler knew that his words were like a knife in the master's heart, but he hoped that at last Beethoven might be persuaded to give up the guardianship of Karl.

"If your good nature had not so often gotten the better of your firmness," he went on earnestly, "you would have driven him away long ago."

Beethoven sighed again, then gave a start as he saw the figure of a child slip through the doorway.

Young Gerhard von Breuning approached with a look of sympathy on his small face. "Mother asked me to deliver this," he said, holding out a note. "She says the poor gentleman must not stay too much alone," he explained to Schindler. "She wishes him to eat his meals with us. I am to fetch him now."

Beethoven read the note through and smiled at the boy with affection.

"Very well, young 'trousers-button,' I will come," he said, and reached for the battered old hat that Karl had made so much fun of.

When they arrived at the Breunings' home, Stephan

in his turn tried to persuade Beethoven to give up Karl's guardianship.

"There is only one thing to be done for the boy," he exclaimed, his hand on the master's shoulder. "He must enter military service. There he will be under the strictest discipline."

Beethoven protested with feeling. "But that would be such a hard life for him!"

Breuning was firm in his insistence. "A military life will be the best training for one who cannot endure freedom!"

Karl was finally persuaded to go into the army, and Breuning agreed to make the necessary arrangements. The magistrate, however, insisted that Karl must leave the city until the preparations for his new career were arranged.

Johann van Beethoven, who had become a landowner in Gneixendorf, happened to be in Vienna at the time. After long years of miserly saving he had bought a large estate in the country, but he still had two payments to make on the purchase.

"Why don't you bring Karl to my home?" he suggested to his brother. "I will charge you nothing for the first fortnight," he continued shrewdly. "If I were not so hard pressed with taxes I would do more."

When Beethoven and his nephew arrived at Gneixendorf they found a dreary stone house awaiting them with large cold rooms which were almost impossible to heat. The master fell ill immediately and during the weeks that followed continued in miserable health.

But in spite of this, he was not idle. Just before leaving Vienna an idea had occurred to him for another quartet. It was his last, and the shortest one of all. The finale grew out of a repartee which, to the musically minded master, had an amusingly rhythmical twist.

"Must it be?" asked a friend when required to hand over some money.

"It must be!" came the answer.

And when Beethoven's housekeeper applied for her weekly allowance, the master jokingly inquired, "Must it be?"—to which she likewise replied, "It must be." Beethoven was so amused that he proceeded to write out a canon of question and answer—then later used the same theme for the ending of his F Major Quartet (Opus 135). He entitled it "The Difficult Resolve."

Beethoven's antics while at work, during those weeks at Gneixendorf, were the wonder and amusement of the countryside. Johann's cook, who made up the master's bed, would burst into laughter when she heard him muttering and growling—which was his way of singing —and beating time with his feet. One day while he was walking through the fields, shouting and waving his arms about, he frightened a team of oxen so badly that they bolted into the fields. No sooner had the peasant gotten his beasts back on the road than the same thing happened again.

"Who was that crazy fool?" he asked indignantly of Johann van Beethoven. "Your *brother?* . . . A pretty brother *that* is!"

Karl meanwhile was loafing about and enjoying himself with the country wenches. He was in no hurry to end the visit. He knew a little of the hardship he would meet in his new life in the army. The fortnight that Breuning had allotted him lengthened into two months, and still he insisted that he was not strong enough to return.

Johann began to regret his invitation. He feared he would have his brother and Karl on his hands indefinitely. "It's high time Karl returned to Vienna," he told Beethoven.

But the master could not bear to part with the boy. "He must have time to grow really well again," he insisted.

Johann was indignant. "You are too easy with him," he exclaimed. "He is quite able to go now. I think you should plan to start next Monday."

Beethoven's irritable temper rose, and he argued violently with his brother. But his angry words only strengthened Johann's determination to be rid of the two, and when finally the master set out with Karl for Vienna, his brother grudgingly ordered his poorest carriage for them.

It was a wet, raw day in late November, and the wind blew fiercely in icy blasts. Beethoven shivered as he climbed into the rickety open vehicle. He thought with dread of the long trip ahead of them and wondered how he could ever stand the ride.

CHAPTER XXI

WITH THE IMMORTALS

(1 8 2 7)

IS IT MUCH FARTHER, now?" Beethoven asked feebly as the carriage jolted endlessly onward and the wind whistled through its open sides.

Karl growled ill-humoredly under his breath. He was too much concerned with his own discomfort to care how miserable his uncle might be. "We'll reach Vienna in a couple of hours, if this plagued vehicle holds together that long," he exclaimed sourly.

Beethoven hunched lower in the carriage seat and tried to pull the shawl closer over his shaking shoulders. The two days' journey from Gneixendorf had been a nightmare to him in his weakened condition. A biting drizzle of late November rain, blown by the gusts of wind through the carriage, had followed them remorselessly. Then came a night spent at a miserable inn along the way, where Beethoven was forced to sleep in a damp, cold room. He had awakened in the night with a high fever followed by a violent chill that set him coughing—dry, hacking spasms that left him weak and helpless.

Then another weary day of driving in the cold. When they finally reached Vienna, Beethoven had hardly strength enough to climb up the stairs to his rooms in the Schwarzspanierhaus—the "Black Spaniard's House."

Karl thought of nothing but rejoining his companions after his long absence from the city. His uncle saw him leave with dismay.

"You will be back soon?" he asked anxiously.

The youth fumbled a moment with the doorknob. "I must get my things together, you know," he answered evasively. "If I am to join my military company so soon, there will be many preparations to make. . . ."

Beethoven nodded. "Yes—but I am ill; I must have someone to attend me. Send me a physician, and tell Herr von Breuning or else Schindler to come to me."

But two days passed before Karl sent the doctor to attend his uncle. Dr. Wawruch, one of Vienna's most skillful physicians, was a musician in his leisure hours and had long admired Beethoven. He hurried to the master's bedside.

"But how does it happen, my dear sir, that you have been so long without attention?" he exclaimed when he found the great man with a serious case of pneumonia.

Beethoven shook his head drearily. "When we grow old and feeble they all desert us," he said in deep dejection. "Vienna has forgotten me—my own relatives forsake me—and even my friends!" He sank back against the pillow, the tears streaming weakly from his eyes.

Wawruch was indignant. "Surely your friends are not aware of your condition," he remarked.

A gleam of light came to the master's eyes. "Perhaps *they* weren't notified either," he exclaimed hopefully.

Breuning and Schindler, shocked by learning of the master's lonely misery, hastened to his bedside and assured him of their love and interest.

"We didn't know, Ludwig," Stephan began, his eyes full of distress.

Schindler busied himself in making the master comfortable. "It is incredible that Karl should have deserted you," he exclaimed angrily. "*I* shall not leave you as long as you need me."

The two men did everything in their power to help him to get better, but in spite of their untiring efforts Beethoven did not improve. The inflammation of the lungs passed into a severe attack of dropsy, and his suffering became intense.

"Can nothing be done to relieve him?" Breuning asked Dr. Wawruch anxiously.

The physician shook his head. "Nothing but an operation to draw off the water," he answered, "and that will be only a temporary relief."

It was before the day of anesthetics, but Beethoven endured the operation bravely. When the water spurted out, he even attempted a feeble joke. "Professor," he said, "you remind me of Moses striking the rock with his staff. . . . Better water from my belly than from my pen!"

The "Professor" (as doctors were then called) complimented him on his fortitude. "You bore yourself like a knight!"

Weeks went by, but, instead of improving, Beethoven grew steadily worse. It became necessary to perform a second operation, then a third, and finally a fourth.

Schindler and Breuning continued to wait on the master and relieve him in every way they could, and little Gerhard spent long hours at his bedside. Beethoven's old friend the Baron Zmeskall, who had been confined to his home for some time with gout, sent delicacies to the sick man and frequent messages of loving interest.

Beethoven replied with a note in his own hand. He had no heart left for the old nonsensical style which he had been accustomed to use in writing to Zmeskall, but the affection for his friend was as strong as ever.

A thousand thanks for your sympathy [he wrote]. I do not despair. The most painful feature is the cessation of all activity. No evil without its good side. May heaven but grant you amelioration of your painful existence. Perhaps health is coming to both of us and we shall meet again in friendly intimacy.

Schindler approached the master's bedside one morning with a large box of books. "Here is a gift from Herr Stumpff in London," he said. "A complete edition of Händel's works!"

Beethoven smiled with pleasure. "What a charming surprise!" He reached out his hand and took the books with keen appreciation. "I have wanted them for a long time. Händel is the greatest, the ablest composer that ever lived! I can still learn much from him."

Whenever his strength would permit he liked to prop up the heavy books of Händel on his bed and look through them. They brought him great joy during the dark days when he was unable to work on his own compositions.

Karl had gone to join his military company, and Beethoven was relieved to know that at last his nephew was safely taken care of. He still felt the tenderest love for the ungrateful boy, and as his condition grew worse he desired to make certain that Karl should be cared for after his death.

He wrote to his friend Dr. Bach about the disposition of his property.

Vienna, Wednesday, January 3, 1827

Before my death I declare my beloved nephew my sole and universal heir of all the property which I possess, chiefly seven bank shares and whatever money may be on hand. If the laws prescribe a modification in this I beg of you as far as possible to turn it to his *advantage.* I appoint you his *curator* and beg his guardian, Court Councilor von Breuning, to take the place of a father to him. God preserve you. A thousand thanks for the love and friendship which you have shown me.

LUDWIG VAN BEETHOVEN

Schindler, who had taken the letter from Beethoven's dictation, looked at the master reflectively. Finally he spoke to him with some hesitation.

"I have just paid the rent, sir, and the apothecary has presented his bill. Are you—have you other money coming in?"

Beethoven looked up with somber eyes. "Not unless I can work!" He frowned helplessly. "Give me my notebook—and another pencil. I must finish my tenth symphony."

Schindler handed them to him with a sigh. He knew how impossible it would be for the master to work in his sick, weakened condition.

In a few moments Beethoven laid down his pencil wearily. "It is no use! The ideas are all confused. . . ." He stared moodily before him for a long time. "What is to become of me, Schindler?" he said pitifully. "If this keeps up, how shall I manage to exist?"

Schindler had been puzzling over the situation, too. "There are many of your friends who would be glad to help you," he began.

Beethoven's eyes flashed for a moment with the old spirit. "I do not beg!" he exclaimed proudly.

Schindler thought again. "You still have the seven bank shares."

Beethoven groaned. "I cannot—I must not use *those*. What would my poor boy have left if I should dispose of the sole inheritance I have for him?"

There was silence for a moment. Finally Schindler made another suggestion. "The Philharmonic Society of London once spoke of giving a concert in your behalf."

Beethoven looked up with sudden inspiration.

"Write down a letter for me to Herr Stumpff," he commanded.

Schindler drew up a chair and wrote at the master's dictation.

How great a joy to receive the works of Händel of which you made me a present—for me a royal present!—this my pen cannot describe. . . . Unfortunately I have been down with the dropsy since the third of December. You can imagine in what a situation this places me! I live generally only from the proceeds of my brain, to make provision of all things for myself and my Karl. Unhappily for a month and a half I have not been able to write a note. . . .

I recall that several years ago the Philharmonic Society wanted to give a concert for my benefit. It would be fortunate for me if they would do this now. It might save me from all the needs that confront me. . . .

While thanking you again for your glorious gift, I beg of you to command me if I can be of service to you here in any way, I shall do it with all my heart. . . .

"A letter from the Philharmonic Society," Schindler announced on the morning of March 18.

Beethoven, who had been anxiously awaiting the letter, seized it eagerly, but found himself unable to tear it open. "Read it to me!" he commanded hoarsely.

The Philharmonic Society [Schindler read] resolved to express their good will and lively sympathy by requesting your acceptance of 100 pounds sterling to provide the necessary comforts and conveniences during your illness. This money will be paid to your order by Mr. Rau, of the house of Eskeles, either in separate sums or all at once, as you desire.

The slow tears coursed down Beethoven's cheeks as Schindler concluded.

"What rare generosity!" he cried. "How noble the English are! Little the Viennese care, for all I might be dying!" he added bitterly.

He had insisted that morning that Schindler and Breuning move him into his armchair, where he could look out of the window once more. They put his long gray dressing gown around him and lifted him tenderly into his chair. He sat there quietly, head bowed and shaggy gray locks falling in disorder about his emaciated shoulders.

"Write down my answer to the Philharmonic Society at once," he said to Schindler. "They shall know how I value their liberality!"

I cannot describe to you in words with what feelings I read your letter. The generosity with which the Philharmonic Society anticipated my petition has touched me in the innermost depths of my soul. I beg you therefore to transmit my sincerest thanks for the particular sympathy and help. . . .

Concerning the concert which the Philharmonic Society has resolved to give, I beg the Society not to abandon this noble purpose, and to deduct the 1,000 florins already sent to me from the proceeds of the concert. And if the Society is disposed graciously to send me the balance I pledge myself to return my heartiest thanks to the Society by binding myself to compose for it either a new symphony, which lies already sketched in my desk, a new overture, or whatever else the Society shall wish.

May heaven very soon restore me again to health, and I will prove to the generous Englishmen how greatly I appreciate their interest in my sad fate. Their noble act will never be forgotten by me. . . .

There was a gentle knock at the door, and a childish voice called from outside: "May I come in?" Schindler opened the door and admitted Gerhard von Breuning. Beethoven's eyes lit up at sight of the boy, and Gerhard in his turn exclaimed with happiness when he saw that the master was sitting up in his chair.

"Thou art better, Uncle Ludwig!" he wrote joyfully on the tablet under the master's hand.

The sick man smiled sadly and looked long out of the window where the first signs of spring were beginning to show.

"Sometimes I think I shall recover," he said slowly, "but in my heart I know the end is not far off." He placed his hand affectionately on the boy's head. "My day's work is done. . . ."

Gerhard seized the master's hand with a sob. "No—no!" he cried. "The doctor will cure thee."

Beethoven smiled again with infinite sadness. "If there were a physician who could help me now, his name would be called 'Wonderful'!"

Schindler approached the master with a message. "Herr Schubert is waiting outside. Do you feel able to see him?"

Beethoven looked up with quick pleasure. "Franz Schubert!" he exclaimed. "Show him in—show him in! This is the man Schindler has talked so much of, do you remember, Gerhard?" The boy nodded.

The door opened to admit a stout, round-faced, dark-haired young man with horn-rimmed spectacles and a shy, retiring manner. He looked reverently at the master and advanced softly, a large portfolio under his arm.

Beethoven welcomed him with open arms. "So this is

Franz Schubert," he exclaimed kindly. "They tell me you are a singer of songs unparalleled!"

Schubert began a modest denial, then remembered Beethoven's sad affliction.

"If my poor efforts meet with *your* approval, sir," he wrote quickly, "I shall feel that they are not unworthy!"

Beethoven looked over the songs—many of them were still in manuscript—with growing interest. He hummed some of the passages over to himself and became more and more enthusiastic.

"Truly, you have the divine spark," he exclaimed with admiration. "Yes, you will move the world with your songs! More, perhaps," he added with a touch of sadness, "than my own music ever can."

Schubert exclaimed at such a sacrilege.

"Ah, well," Beethoven rejoined with a laugh, "they do not understand my music now, but some day it will please them!" He sank back wearily in his chair, and Schindler motioned that the interview was at an end.

As Schubert left the room he cast a last look at the master. Beethoven sat quietly, his hand held between Gerhard's two strong young palms, and his eyes fixed thoughtfully on the child's face. On his lips was a gentle smile, as if he saw the countenance of his first love mirrored in the boy's eyes.

During the next few days the master failed rapidly, and on the morning of March 24 it became evident that the end was not far off. Beethoven was unconscious most of the time, but in his rare intervals of wakening something seemed to be troubling him.

He beckoned Stephan von Breuning to his side. "You —have been a true friend, Stephan," he whispered heavily. "Care for my poor boy—when I am gone. . . ."

"Yes, yes, Ludwig!" Breuning answered brokenly.

"The bank shares—" Beethoven continued feebly— "they are hidden here." Breuning bent over in a vain effort to catch the last words, but the master had fallen back, unconscious once more.

"He wishes us to find the bank shares for Karl," Schindler exclaimed. "I once heard him say something about a secret hiding place."

The two men began searching vainly through the room, while Beethoven lay unconscious on his bed, breathing heavily.

Breuning's glance was attracted by a small oil painting of a beautiful young girl in Grecian costume that hung above Beethoven's desk. "Do you know whose likeness this is?"

Schindler shook his head while Breuning turned the portrait over curiously. "Look!" he exclaimed. "There is an inscription on the back." And he read the irregular characters:

TO THE UNIQUE GENIUS

TO THE GREAT ARTIST

TO THE GOOD MAN

FROM T. B.

He studied the portrait carefully. "T. B.," he said reflectively. "I wonder if it could be Therese von Brunswick. He loved her very deeply at one time, of that I am certain." He thought for a moment. "But there was the Countess Giulietta—and there were others. . . ."

Beethoven, still unconscious, sighed heavily. Stephan went over and gazed down at him in deepest sorrow. This man, in spite of all the misunderstandings that had come between them, had been his friend for forty years. He could not bear the thought of losing him. But it proved only a short separation, for two months later Breuning himself passed away.

It was not until after Beethoven's death that the bank shares were found. Quite by accident Holz, a young musician who had been devoted to the master, discovered a secret, inner drawer in Beethoven's desk. Within was a dusty packet containing the seven bank shares and three letters in Beethoven's handwriting, their yellowed sheets almost illegible. The first letter began: "My angel, my all, my very self"—the last spoke in impassioned terms to his "Immortal Beloved." But there was no name—nothing to indicate to whom the letters had been written. And not even his closest friends ever knew the identity of Beethoven's "Immortal Beloved."

A storm shook the city of Vienna on the afternoon of March 26, 1827. The snow fell in heavy flakes, and there was a succession of violent thunder claps. Lightning flashed across the sky and lit up the interior of a wretched room in the Schwarzspanierhaus where, in the midst of poverty and neglect, one of the world's great souls lay dying.

The thunder rolled out in low peals, like the distant echoes of some heavenly orchestra. All at once the dying man raised himself slightly, as if he heard something in the distance. His poor ears, long closed to earthly sounds, were opened now to the divine harmonies which had so deeply moved him in his childhood and which he had spent his life in trying to recapture.

A look of intense joy came over his face. He lifted his right arm slowly and clenched his fist with a last gesture of determination—then sank back upon his bed while the lightning illuminated his features with brief radiance.

Once more a deafening crash filled the air, reverberating through the skies like a mighty welcome from the spirits of Nature to one who belonged to them. And the deep tones of the thunder carried a new name to add to the list of the immortals:

BEETHOVEN

APPENDICES

BIBLIOGRAPHY

THAYER, ALEXANDER WHEELOCK. *The Life of Ludwig van Beethoven,* edited by Henry Edward Krehbiel. G. Schirmer, Inc., New York, 1921.

SCHAUFFLER, ROBERT HAVEN. *Beethoven, the Man Who Freed Music.* Doubleday, Doran & Co., New York, 1929.

SONNECK, O. G. *Beethoven: Impressions of Contemporaries.* G. Schirmer, Inc., New York, 1927.

ROLLAND, ROMAIN. *Beethoven,* translated by Constance Hull. Henry Holt and Company, New York, 1917.

ROLLAND, ROMAIN. *Beethoven the Creator,* translated by Ernest Newman. Harper & Bros., New York, 1929.

SCHINDLER, ANTON FELIX. *The Life of Beethoven,* edited by Ignaz Moscheles. Oliver Ditson Company, Boston.

NOHL, LOUIS. *Life of Beethoven,* translated by John J. Lalor. A. C. McClurg & Company, Chicago, 1881.

MASON, DANIEL GREGORY. *Beethoven and His Forerunners.* The Macmillan Company, New York, 1904.

BEETHOVEN WORKS AND RECORDINGS

NOTE.—*In the following list will be found the recordings now available in American record shops. Many others have, of course, been made in the past; that these are not listed here is because they are European records that have not been imported during recent years. Many of them will gradually become available as they are re-pressed in this country. It is therefore worth while to ask your dealer about them.*

OPUS NO.   RECORD NO.

1. Three Trios for piano, violin, and 'cello, in E-flat, G, and C Minor (See Opus 104)
2. Three Sonatas for piano, in F minor, A, and C
   (All the piano sonatas are recorded by Artur Schnabel in the albums of the Beethoven Sonata Society; not sold separately.)
3. Trio for violin, viola, and 'cello, in E-flat
4. Quintet for 2 violins, 2 violas, and 'cello, in E-flat (See Opus 103)
5. Two Sonatas for 'cello and piano
   No. 1, in F, Casals and Horszowski   VM-843
   No. 2, in G minor, Piatigorsky and Schnabel   VM-281
6. Sonata for piano 4-hands, in D
7. Sonata for piano, in E-flat
   See note under Opus 2
8. Serenade (trio) for violin, viola, and 'cello, in D (See Opus 42)
   Pasquier Trio   CM-341
   Goldberg, Hindemith, and Feuermann   CM-217
9. Three Trios for violin, viola, and 'cello, in G, D, and C minor
   No. 3 in C minor, Pasquier Trio   CM-379
10. Three Sonatas for piano, in C minor, F, and D
    See note under Opus 2
11. Trio for piano, clarinet (or violin), and 'cello, in B-flat
12. Three Sonatas for violin and piano, in D, A, and E-flat

330

No. 3, in E-flat, J. Heifetz and E. Bay   VM-852
   (All the violin-and-piano sonatas are recorded
     by Fritz Kreisler and Franz Rupp in the
     albums of the Beethoven Violin Sonata
     Society; not sold separately)

13. Sonata for piano, in C minor (*Pathétique*)
    See note under Opus 2

14. Two Sonatas for piano, in E and G
    See note under Opus 2

15. Concerto No. 1 for piano and orchestra, in C
    Anita Dorfmann with NBC Symphony Orch.,
     Toscanini   VM-1036
    Schnabel with London Philharmonic Orch.,
     Sargent   VM-158
    Gieseking with Berlin State Opera Orch.,
     Rosbaud   CM-308

16. Quintet for piano, oboe, clarinet, bassoon, and
    French horn, in E-flat

17. Sonata for piano and French horn or 'cello
    Pessl and Freiberg   CMX-86

18. Six String Quartets
    No. 1, in F
     Budapest Quartet   CM-444
     Coolidge Quartet   VM-550
    No. 2, in G
     Budapest Quartet   VM-601
     Coolidge Quartet   VM-622
    No. 3, in D
     Budapest Quartet   VM-289
     Coolidge Quartet   VM-650
    No. 4, in C minor
     Budapest Quartet   CM-556
     Coolidge Quartet   VM-696
    No. 5, in A
     Lener Quartet   CM-301
     Coolidge Quartet   VM-716

28. Sonata for piano (*Pastoral*), in D
    See note under Opus 2
29. Quintet for 2 violins, 2 violas, and 'cello, in C
    Members of Lener Quartet with W. Primrose   CM-294
30. Three Sonatas for violin and piano
    No. 1, in A, Lener and Kentner   CLX-827/9
    No. 2, in C minor
        Busch and Serkin   VM-283
        Y. and H. Menuhin   VM-1008
    No. 3, in G
        Milstein and Balsam   CMX-137
        Heifetz and Bay   VM-570
31. Three Sonatas for piano, in G, D minor, and E-flat
    No. 2, in D minor, Gieseking   CMX-39
32. Song, *An die Hoffnung*
33. Seven Bagatelles for piano, in E-flat, C, F, A, C,
    D, and A-flat
        No. 1, in E-flat, Gieseking   C-69478D
        No. 2, in C, Eileen Joyce   CDX-974
34. Six Variations on an original theme, for piano, in F
    Claudio Arrau   VDM-892
    (also by Schnabel in Society Albums)
35. Fifteen Variations with a fugue, on theme from
    Prometheus, for piano, in E-flat (also called
    Eroica Variations)
    Claudio Arrau   VDM-892
    (also by Schnabel in Society Albums)
36. Symphony No. 2, in D
    Pittsburgh Symphony Orch., Reiner   CM-597
    London Philharmonic Orch., Beecham   CM-302
    London Symphony Orch., Weingartner   CM-377
    Boston Symphony Orch., Koussevitzky   VM-625
37. Concerto No. 3 for piano and orchestra, in C minor
    A. Rubinstein with NBC Symphony Orch.,
        Toscanini   VM-1016
    Schnabel with London Philharmonic Orch.,
        Sargent   VM-194

OPUS NO.   RECORD NO.

51. Two Rondos for piano, in C and G
    No. 1, in C, Schnabel   V-14322

52. Eight Songs: *Urians Reise; Feuerfarb; Das Lied-
chen v. d. Ruhe; Mailied; Molly's Abschied; Die
Liebe; Marmotte; Das Blümchen wunderhold*

53. Sonata for piano, in C (*Waldstein*) (See also Opus
    \70)
    Gieseking   CM-358
    See also note under Opus 2

54. Sonata for piano, in F
    See note under Opus 2

55. Symphony No. 3 in E-flat (*Eroica*)
    N. Y. Philharmonic Symphony Orch., Walter   CM-449
    Vienna Philharmonic Orch., Weingartner   CM-285
    NBC Symphony Orch., Toscanini   VM-765
    London Philharmonic Orch., Koussevitzky   VM-263

56. Triple Concerto for piano, violin, 'cello, and orchestra, in C
    Morales (piano), Odnoposoff (violin), Auber
    ('cello), and Vienna Philharmonic Orch.,
    Weingartner   CM-327

57. Sonata for piano, in F minor (*Appassionata*)
    Gieseking   CM-365
    Serkin   VM-583
    Fischer   VM-279
    See also note under Opus 2

58. Concerto No. 4 for piano and orchestra, in G
    Schnabel with London Philharmonic Orch.,
    Sargent   VM-156
    Schnabel with Chicago Symphony Orch., Stock VDM-930
    Gieseking with Saxon State Orch., Böhm   CM-411

59. Three String Quartets (*Rasumowsky*)
    No. 1, in F
        Busch Quartet   CM-543
        Roth Quartet   CM-256
        Coolidge Quartet   VM-804

No. 2, in E minor
Budapest Quartet   VM-340
Coolidge Quartet   VDM-919
No. 3, in C
Budapest Quartet   CM-510
Busch Quartet   VM-171

60. Symphony No. 4, in B-flat
BBC Symphony Orch., Toscanini   VM-676
London Philharmonic Orch., Weingartner   CM-197

61. Concerto for violin and orchestra, in D
Szigeti with British Symphony Orch., Walter   CM-177
Heifetz with NBC Symphony Orch., Toscanini   VM-705
Kreisler with London Philharmonic Orch.,
Barbirolli   VM-325

62. Overture to *Coriolanus*
London Symphony Orch., Walter   V-12535
Minneapolis Symphony Orch., Mitropoulos   C-11175D
NBC Symphony Orch., Toscanini   V-119023

63. Arrangement of Opus 4 as trio for piano and strings
64. Arrangement of Opus 3 for piano and 'cello
65. Scena and aria, *Ah, perfido!*
K. Flagstad, Philadelphia Orchestra, Ormandy   VM-439
66. Twelve Variations on *Ein Mädchen* (from Mozart's
Magic Flute), for 'cello and piano
67. Symphony No. 5, in C minor
Berlin Philharmonic Orch., Furtwängler   VM-426
London Philharmonic Orch., Weingartner   CM-245
N. Y. Philharmonic Symphony Orch., Walter   CM-498
NBC Symphony Orch., Toscanini   VM-640
London Philharmonic Orch., Koussevitzky   VM-245
All-American Youth Orch., Stokowski   CM-451
68. Symphony No. 6, in F (*Pastoral*)
N. Y. City Symphony Orch., Stokowski   VM-1032
BBC Symphony Orch., Toscanini   VM-417
Vienna Philharmonic Orch., Walter   VG-20
Minneapolis Symphony Orch., Mitropoulos   CM-401
69. Sonata for 'cello and piano, in A
Casals and Schulhof   VM-134

    Schnabel with Chicago Symphony Orch., Stock   VDM-939

74. String Quartet, in E-flat (*Harp*)

    Budapest Quartet   VM-467

    Lener Quartet   CM-202

75. Six Songs: *Kennst du das Land; Herz, mein Herz; Es war einmal; Mit Liebesblick; Einst Wohnten; Zwar schuf das Glück,* for soprano and piano

76. Six Variations for piano, in D

77. Fantaisie for piano, in G minor

78. Sonata for piano, in F-sharp

    Egon Petri   C-68939D

    See also note under Opus 2

79. Sonatina for piano, in G

80. Fantasia for piano, orchestra, and chorus, in C minor, on Beethoven's song *Gegenliebe*

81a. Sonata for piano, in E-flat (*Les Adieux*)

    A. Rubinstein   VM-858

    See also note under Opus 2

81b. Sextet for 2 violins, viola, 'cello, and 2 French horns, in E-flat

82. Four Ariettas and Duet for soprano and tenor: *Dimmi, ben mio; T'intendo; Che fa, il mio bene* (buffa); *che fa, il mio bene* (seria); *Odi, l'aura*

83. Three Songs for soprano: *Trocknet nicht* (or *Wonne der Wehmut*); *Was zieht mir; Kleine Blumen* (or *Mit einem gemalten Bande*)

    No. 1, *Wonne der Wehmut,* E. Schumann   V-1836

    No. 3, *Mit einem gemalten Bande,* E. Schumann   V-1836

84. Music to Goethe's *Egmont:* Overture; Song, *Die Trommel;* Entr'acte I; Entr'acte II; Song, *Freudvoll und Leidvoll;* Entr'acte III; *Clärchens Tod;* Melodrama; *Siegessymphonie*

    Overture

    Vienna Philharmonic Orch., Weingartner   C-69195D

    Songs

    Lotte Lehmann and orch.   D-20380

OPUS NO.	RECORD NO.
arr. piano, Rachmaninoff	V-1196
arr. 2 pianos, Bartlett and Robertson	C-17198D
114. March and Chorus from *The Ruins of Athens*	
For recording of March, see above	
115. Overture in C, sometimes called *Namensfeier*	
116. Terzetto, *Tremate,* for soprano, tenor, and bass	
117. *King Stephen,* Overture and nine numbers	
118. Elegiac Song for soprano, alto, tenor, bass, and strings	
119. Bagatelles for piano (thirteen)	
No. 11 in A, Myra Hess	C-4083M
120. Thirty-three Variations on a waltz by Diabelli	
121a. Variations on *Ich bin der Schneider Kakadu* for piano, violin, and 'cello	
Danish Quartet	VM-729
121b. *Opferlied,* for soprano with chorus and orchestra	
122. *Bundeslied,* for soprano, alto, chorus, and wind	
123. Mass in D (*Missa Solemnis*)	
Harvard Glee Club, Radcliffe Choral Society, E. Power Biggs (organ), Boston Symphony Orch. under Koussevitzky, and soloists. In two volumes	VM-758
124. Overture, *Consecration of the House,* in C	
London Philharmonic Orch., Weingartner	CMX-140
Boston "Pops" Orch., Fiedler	VM-618
125. Symphony No. 9, in D minor	
Philadelphia Orch., Stokowski, with Univ. of Penna. Choral Society and soloists	VM-296
Vienna Philharmonic Orch., Weingartner, with Vienna State Opera Chorus and soloists	CM-227
126. Bagatelles for piano (six)	
No. 6 in E-flat	
E. Erdmann	D-25783
127. String Quartet in E-flat	
Budapest Quartet	CM-537
Busch Quartet	VM-489
128. Arietta, *The Kiss*	
E. Wolff	C-4210M

*The works that follow had no opus numbers, the latter
being added by Sir George Grove*

FOR ORCHESTRA OR ORCHESTRAL INSTRUMENTS

OPUS NO.

183. Six easy Variations in F on a Swiss air, for piano or harp

184. Eight Variations in C on Grétry's air *Une fièvre brulante*, for piano

185. Ten Variations in B-flat on Salieri's air, *La Stessa, la Stessissima,* for piano

186. Seven Variations in F on Winter's quartet, *Kind, willst du,* for piano

187. Eight Variations in F on Süssmayer's trio, *Tändeln und scherzen,* for piano

188. Six very easy Variations in G on an original theme for piano

189. Seven Variations in C on *God Save the King,* for piano

190. Five Variations in D on *Rule, Britannia,* for piano

191. Thirty-two Variations in C minor for piano   V1689/90
      Horowitz

192. Eight Variations in B-flat on *Ich hab' ein kleines Hüttchen nur* for piano

WORKS FOR VOICES

193. Bass Solo *Germania!* with chorus and orchestra

194. Bass Solo *Es ist vollbracht* with chorus and orchestra

195. Miserere and Amplius, dirge at Beethoven's funeral, 4-voice men's chorus with 4 trombones. Adapted by Seyfried from two of three ms. Equali for trombones

196a. Cantata on the death of the Emperor Joseph II for soli, chorus, orchestra

196b. Cantata *Er schlummert,* on the accession of Leopold II

197. Song of the monks from Schiller's *Wilhelm Tell, Rasch tritt der Tod,* for 2 tenors and bass

198. Chorus, *O Hoffnung* (4 bars) for the Archduke Rudolph

199. Cantata in E-flat for soprano, alto, bass, and piano

OPUS NO.   RECORD NO.
246. Song, *Die stille Nacht*
247. Song, *O dass ich dir*
247a. Another setting of the above
248. Song, *Dort auf dem hohen Felsen*
249. Song, *Wenn ich ein Vöglein wär*
250. Song, *Wo blüht das Blümchen*
251. Song, *Nord oder Süd*
252. Song, *Lisch aus, mein Licht*
253. Song, *Wenn die Sonne nieder sinket*
254. Two songs, *Seufzer eines Ungelieben* and *Gegenliebe*
255. Song, *Turteltaube*
256. Song, *Gedenke mein! ich denke dein*
257. "Jena" Symphony, in C (authenticity doubtful)
    Berlin State Opera Orch., Weissmann   D-25459/61
258. Allegro and Menuetto for 2 flutes, in G
259. Trio for piano, flute, and bassoon, in G

RECORDINGS UNIDENTIFIED BY OPUS NUMBER

Duo for viola and 'cello (with eyeglasses obbligato), in
    E-flat
    Primrose and Feuermann   V11-8620
Trio for 2 oboes and English horn, variations on
    Mozart's *La ci darem la mano*
    Wann, Prior, and Brenner   Musicraft
                                                   Set 34

Gavotte for piano, in F (originally piano 4-hands)
    arr. piano solo, Harold Bauer   V-6592
    arr. violin and piano, Kreisler and Lamson   V-1136

THE WORLD THAT BEETHOVEN LIVED IN

BEETHOVEN'S LIFE	MUSICAL EVENTS	WORLD EVENTS
1770 Born at Bonn on December 16.	1770 Tartini dies. Mozart (aged 14), in Rome with his father, writes out the score of Allegri's *Miserere* after a single hearing.	1770 Born, Wordsworth, Wm. Clark (American explorer). Discovery of Australia by Capt. Cook. Boston Massacre; Crispus Attucks killed.
	1772 B, Mälzel (inventor of metronome), Prince Lobkowitz, friend and patron of Beethoven. Gluck goes to Paris. Mozart produces opera *Lucio Silla.*	1772 First "partition of Poland" (Austria, Russia, Prussia). In Boston Saml. Adams org. first of the colonial Committees of Correspondence.
1773 Death of his grandfather.	1773 Clementi's sonatas ded. to Haydn establish the form of the pianoforte sonata. Grétry's *Céphale et Procris.*	1773 Wm. Henry Harrison b. Boone settles in Kentucky. Boston Tea Party.
1774 Begins music study. Birth of his brother Carl.	1774 Gluck, in Paris, produces his *Orfeo* (revised) and *Iphigénie en Aulide.*	1774 D, Goldsmith, Louis XV. Louis XVI succeeds. Priestley discovers oxygen. First Continental Congress.
	1775 D, Giovanni Sammartini. Haydn's oratorio *Il ritorno di Tobia* produced in Vienna. Mozart's operas *Il re pastore* and *La finta giardiniera.*	1775 B, Charles Lamb, Jane Austen. With battles of Concord, Lexington, and Bunker Hill, the American Revolution opens.
1776 Birth of his brother Johann.	1776 Vienna National Theater founded. Gluck produces *Alceste* in Paris.	1776 Decl. of Independence signed. B. Franklin goes to Paris for 9 years.
1778 Plays at a concert for the first time. Has a few organ lessons from Van den Eeden.	1778 D, Thomas Arne. B, Hummel, Kraft ('cellist of Schuppanzigh Quartet). Vienna Singspiel founded.	1778 D, Voltaire, Rousseau, elder Pitt. France recog. Amer. independence, signs alliance. Battle of Monmouth.

1779 Capt. Cook killed in Hawaii. Battle between *Bonhomme Richard* (John Paul Jones) and *Serapis*.

1780 B, Francis Scott Key. On death of Maria Theresa, Joseph II becomes emperor.

1781 Battle of Cowpens; siege of Yorktown; surrender of British. Herschel discovers Uranus. Rousseau's *Confessions* published.

1782 B, Froebel, Calhoun, D. Webster, Van Buren. Britain signs prelim. peace with U. S. First English Bible printed in America is publ. by Aiken.

1783 Treaty of Paris signed; powers recog. independence of U. S. In Paris, the Montgolfier brothers make first ascent in first hot-air balloon.

1784 D., Saml. Johnson, Fr. Junipero Serra. B, Ludwig Spohr, Leigh Hunt, Palmerston. Jefferson's *Notes on the State of Virginia* published.

1779 Gluck's opera *Iphigénie en Tauride*, Haydn's *L'isola disabitata* produced.

1780 Grétry's opera *Andromaque*, Paris. New theater at Esterház is opened with Haydn's *La fedelta premiata*.

1781 B, Diabelli. Mozart prod. *Idomeneo* in Munich; settles in Vienna; leaves Archbishop's service; his friendship with Haydn begins.

1782 D., Johann Christian Bach, Metastasio. B, Paganini, Auber. Mozart produces *Die Entführung aus dem Serail*; marries Constanze Weber.

1783 D., Kirnberger, Johann Adolf Hasse, Caffarelli, Padre Antonio Soler.

1784 D, Padre Martini, Wilhelm Friedemann Bach. B, Ludwig Spohr, Ferdinand Ries. Mozart, Haydn, and others play chamber music together in Vienna.

1779 Begins clavier study under Pfeiffer; other subjects with Zambona.

1780 Continues study of organ with Van den Eeden.

1781 Leaves school. Composes three pf. sonatas and nine variations on a march by Dressler. Studies music with Neefe, violin with Rovantini.

1782 Neefe, having succeeded Van den Eeden as chapel organist, appoints Beethoven his deputy organist during Neefe's absence.

1783 At 13, appointed cembalo player in the court opera orchestra, with duties in accompanying and conducting. The *Dressler* Variations are published.

1784 The new Elector, Max Franz, makes Beethoven second court organist, with a small salary. Composes some piano and vocal works.

BEETHOVEN'S LIFE	MUSICAL EVENTS	WORLD EVENTS
1785 Studies violin with Franz Ries (Ferdinand's father). Composes a piano trio, piano quartets, a song, etc.	1785 D, Galuppi. B, Milder-Hauptmann, soprano for whom Beethoven wrote the role of Fidelio.	1785 B, Audubon, Oliver Hazard Perry, De Quincey, Bettine von Arnim. Jeffries and Blanchard cross the English Channel by balloon.
1786 His sister, Maria Margaretha, born.	1786 B, Carl Maria von Weber. Haydn comp. his "Paris" Symphonies. Mozart produces *The Marriage of Figaro* and *Der Schauspieldirektor*.	1786 D, Frederick the Great. B, Davy Crockett. Fredk. Wm. II becomes King of Prussia. In London, impeachment of Warren Hastings begins.
1787 On his first visit to Vienna he meets Mozart (aged 31), plays for him, and takes a few lessons. His mother and baby sister die.	1787 D, Gluck, Mozart's father Leopold. In Prague, Mozart's *Don Giovanni* is produced. Haydn composes the six "King of Prussia" Quartets.	1787 B, Guizot, Emma Willard. U. S. Constitution signed; Washington elected President; Hamilton's *Federalist Papers* start publication.
1788 Friendship with Count Waldstein and the Breunings begins. Plays viola in the court orchestra, continuing as assistant court organist.	1788 D, Karl P. E. Bach. In Vienna, Salieri (teacher of Beethoven, Schubert, Liszt), is apptd. court music director. Haydn's *Oxford Symphony*.	1788 D, Buffon, Gainsborough, the Earl of Chatham. B, Byron, Schopenhauer. Andrew Jackson migrates westward from S. Carolina. Goethe's *Egmont* pub.
1789 Is assigned part of the salary given to his father, whose drunkenness is now habitual.	1789 B, Mayseder, violinist of Schuppanzigh Quartet. In Paris, Natl. Guard Band is organized by Sarrette.	1789 B, James Fenimore Cooper. Bastille stormed, opening French Revolution. Mutiny on the *Bounty*. Jay becomes first U. S. Chief Justice.
1790 At Christmas is visited by Salomon and Haydn on their way to London.	1790 D, Haydn's patron, Prince Nicolas Esterházy.	1790 D, Franklin. B, John Tyler, Sarah Josepha Hale, Lamartine, Champollion. Galvani discovers current electricity. U. S. patent system created.

1791 For Count Waldstein, he composes a *Ritterballet* (Opus 149).

1792 On Haydn's second visit to Bonn he praises a cantata of Beethoven's. In November, Beethoven goes to Vienna for good, begins lessons with Haydn. Death of his father.

1793 Accompanies Haydn on a visit to Esterház. Continues studies with Schenk. Meets Baron von Swieten and Prince Lichnowsky.

1794 Studies counterpart with Albrechtsberger, quartet-writing with Förster.

1795 Opus 1 (3 piano trios) published. He plays B-flat Pf. Concerto at first public appearance. Writes *Adelaide* (Opus 46).

1791 D., Mozart, Paradies. B., Meyerbeer, Czerny. Haydn arrives in England on his first visit; London concerts. Oxford degree; Symphonies 93-96. In Vienna, Mozart produces *The Magic Flute.*

1792 B., Rossini, Lowell Mason. Rouget de Lisle writes words and music of *Marseillaise;* it is taken up as the French armies' marching song. Haydn returns to Vienna from England.

1793 D., Nardini. Paganini (aged 11) gives his first public concert. In Phila., Benj. Orr opens the first music shop in America. First American perf. of Haydn's *Seven Last Words,* N.Y.C.

1794 B., Prince Galitzin (Beethoven's patron), Moscheles. Hewitt's ballad-opera *Tammany* is produced in N.Y.C.

1795 B., A. Schindler, Beethoven's friend and biographer. In Leipzig, music-pub. house of Breitkopf & Härtel is founded. Haydn's 2d visit to England. French National Guard Band's music school is reorganized as the Paris Conservatoire.

1791 D., Mirabeau, John Wesley, Francis Hopkinson. B., Faraday, John Howard Paine, Bunsen, S. F. B. Morse. Design of Washington, D. C., laid out by L'Enfant. Bill of Rights passed. Bank of U. S. founded.

1792 French monarchy abolished; First Republic founded; Revolutionary Armies start European war, Bonaparte (aged 23) being an officer. Pres. Washington lays cornerstone of White House.

1793 D., Hancock, Marat. B., Sam Houston, Stephen Austin. Reign of Terror begins in France; King, Queen, and many notables guillotined. Washington's 2d inaug. Whitney invents cotton gin.

1794 Robespierre and other French leaders guillotined. Kosciusko leads revolution of Poles against Russia. Thomas Paine pub. *The Age of Reason* in Paris. Dr. Priestley emigrates to America.

1795 D., Boswell, Robert Rogers, Cagliostro. B., Keats, Carlyle, Joseph Rodman Drake. In France, the Directory; Bonaparte made commdr. French Army of the Interior. Goethe's *Wilhelm Meister* (Part I) published.

BEETHOVEN'S LIFE	MUSICAL EVENTS	WORLD EVENTS
1796 Visits Prague and Berlin. In Berlin, plays the two 'cello sonatas (Opus 5) before the King. Comp. *Ah, perfido!* and other works.	1796 D, Giardini. In France, Erard's first grand piano made. In N.Y.C., the production of Benjamin Carr's ballad-opera *The Archers of Switzerland.*	1796 D, Empress Catherine II of Russia, Anthony Wayne, Robt. Burns. B, Corot, Horace Mann, Wm. H. Prescott. Dr. Jenner performs first vaccination for smallpox. Burney's *Camilla* published. Washington's Farewell Address.
1797 Publishes *Adelaide.* His early compositions attract attention. Begins to give lessons.	1797 B, Donizetti, Schubert. Austrian natl. anthem composed by Haydn. At 11, Weber begins music study with Michael Haydn. In Paris, Cherubini's opera *Medée*, four operas by Méhul, and three by Grétry.	1797 D, Horace Walpole, Edmund Burke. B, Heine, Mary Lyon. John Adams inaugurated. Bonaparte and French Army make war in Italy against Austrians; by Peace of Campo Formio the Republic of Venice goes out of existence.
1798 Deafness begins. Gives concerts at Prague. Pub. Opus 9 trios, Opus 10 pf. sonatas, Opus 11 trio, and several sets of variations.	1798 D, Pugnani, Giordani, Cannabich. B, Vuillaume, great French violinmaker. In Vienna, Haydn's oratorio *The Creation* first perf. (privately).	1798 D, Vancouver, Galvani, Casanova. B, Auguste Comte, Leopardi, Michelet. At Aboukir Bay (Battle of the Nile) British under Nelson defeat French navy. French occupy Rome.
1799 Publishes three violin-and-pf. sonatas (Opus 12) and Sonata *Pathétique* (Opus 13).	1799 D, Dittersdorf. B, Halévy. Operas by Méhul and Grétry in Paris. First public perf. of Haydn's *Creation,* in Vienna.	1799 D, George Washington, Patrick Henry. B, Balzac, Pushkin, Delacroix. Six French armies overrun Europe. Bonaparte becomes First Consul.
1800 Gives concert at which Sym. No. 1 and Septet (Opus 20) are played. Comp. *Prometheus* ballet music.	1800 Paris Conservatoire reorganized by Bonaparte. Boieldieu's opera *Le Calife de Bagdad* is produced, Paris.	1800 B, Macaulay, Moltke. Congress meets in Washington; Adams moves into the White House. Spain secretly cedes Louisiana Territory to France.

1801 B., Farragut, Brigham Young, Cardinal Newman, Seward. Jefferson's 1st inauguration. French armies continue the conquest of Europe.

1802 B., Hugo, Kossuth, Landseer. Peace of Amiens brings temporary truce in Europe. New French constitution; Elba annexed. Napoleon creates the Legion of Honor.

1803 D., Saml. Adams, Robert Morris. B., Emerson, Bulwer-Lytton, Mérimée, George Sand. Napoleon threatens to invade England. U. S. buys Louisiana Territory from France.

1804 D., Kant, Priestley, Hamilton (in duel with Burr). B., Disraeli, Hawthorne, Franklin Pierce. Napoleon has himself crowned Emperor. Lewis and Clark Expedition starts west.

1805 D., Lord Nelson, Schiller, Cornwallis. B., Hans Christian Andersen, Mazzini, Lesseps, Tocqueville. Jefferson's 2d inaug. Important European battles: Ulm, Trafalgar, Austerlitz; Napoleon occupies Vienna.

1801 D., Stamitz, Cimarosa. B., Bellini. First perf. of Haydn's *The Seasons.* In Paris, Théâtre Italien opened for performances of Italian operas; many operas by Cherubini and Grétry.

1802 Paisiello is apptd. by Napoleon his maître de chapelle. In London, John Stafford Smith made org. of Chapel Royal (composer of tune used by Key for *The Star-Spangled Banner*).

1803 B., H. Berlioz, Karoline Unger (soprano soloist in 1824 première of Beethoven's Ninth and *Missa Solemnis*). Prems. of Cherubini's *Anacréon* and Weber's *Peter Schmoll.*

1804 B., Mikhail Glinka, Johann Strauss the elder, Schröder-Devrient (soprano who sang Leonore in 1822 revival of Beethoven's *Fidelio,* and later created many Wagner roles).

1805 D., Boccherini. B., Manuel P. R. Garcia, great singing teacher (d. 1906). Mozart's librettist Da Ponte leaves Vienna for America; teaches at King's College (later Columbia University).

1801 At the Burgtheater in Vienna, the *Prometheus* ballet is performed. His deafness increases. Falls in love with Giulietta Guicciardi.

1802 At Heiligenstadt he begins composing Symphony No. 2, and writes his "Heiligenstadt Testament."

1803 *The Mount of Olives* (oratorio) is sung, and the *Kreutzer* Sonata perf. by Beethoven and Bridgetower. He meets Vogler and Weber.

1804 Having dedicated his Symphony No. 3 (*Eroica*) to Napoleon, he crosses out the dedication.

1805 Comp. the *Appassionata* Sonata. His opera *Fidelio* is withdrawn after 3 performances and revised. Meets Cherubini.

1806 Opera *Fidelio*, revised, is again performed. Clement introduces the Violin Concerto. The *Eroica* Symphony is published. Writes Symphony No. 4.

1806 B., Henriette Sontag, soprano soloist in première of Beethoven's Ninth Symphony and *Missa Solemnis* (see 1824). At 14, Rossini wins entrance to Bologna Academy.

1806 B., Edwin Forrest, John Stuart Mill, Elizabeth Barrett (Browning). Zebulon Pike discovers Pikes Peak. Lewis and Clark Expedition returns to St. Louis.

1807 Fourth Symphony and *Coriolanus* Overture are produced. Comp. Opus 59 (*Rasumowsky*) quartets.

1807 Premières of Spontini's opera *La Vestale* and Méhul's *Joseph*, in Paris. Pleyel founds his piano factory in Paris.

1807 D., Rochambeau. B., Longfellow, Lee, Garibaldi, Whittier. Burr's trial for treason opens. European war continues; battles of Ulm and Friedland. Fulton's *Clermont* steams from N.Y.C. to Albany in 32 hours.

1808 Finishes Symphonies Nos. 5 and 6.

1808 B., Balfe, Malibran. At 11 Franz Schubert enters training school for court singers and joins court choir. Prince A. Rasumowsky organizes his string quartet, later to be called the Schuppanzigh.

1808 B., Jefferson Davis, Salmon P. Chase. Peninsular War opens in Portugal and Spain between French armies and English under Wellington. U.S. abolishes slave traffic with Africa. Goethe's *Faust*, Scott's *Marmion*, published.

1809 Composes the *Emperor* Pf. Concerto and the *Harp* Quartet. Prince Lobkowitz and the Archduke Rudolph become his patrons and friends.

1809 D., Franz Joseph Haydn. B., Mendelssohn. Schubert becomes first violin in school orchestra. In London, Covent Garden Theatre, burned in 1808, is rebuilt for opera.

1809 B., Lincoln, Gladstone, Darwin, Poe, Kit Carson, O. W. Holmes, Tennyson. Madison inaug. In European war, battles of Corunna, Aspern, Wagram. The French occupy Vienna.

1810 Now 40, he is cut off from friends by almost total deafness. He meets Bettina von Arnim.

1810 B., Chopin, Schumann, Ole Bull, Ferdinand David, Nicolai.

1810 B., Barnum, Musset, Cavour. Wars of S. American liberation begin, Argentina winning independence from Spain.

354

1811 Meets Mälzel, inventor of the metronome. *Emperor* Concerto, *Les Adieux* pf. sonata, *Egmont* Overture, and *The Mount of Olives* published.

1812 On a visit to Teplitz, meets Goethe. Falls in love with the singer Amalie Sebald. Finishes Symphonies Nos. 7 and 8. Publishes the rest of the *Egmont* music.

1813 Visits Baden. Seventh Symphony and *Wellington's Victory* are performed. Is increasingly concerned over the Napoleonic campaigns.

1814 Revises *Fidelio* once more, and it is again performed, this time with the *Fidelio* Overture. Many concerts of his music are given in Vienna with great success.

1811 B., Liszt, Ambroise Thomas, Grisi. Lower Rhine Music Festivals are inaugurated. Schubert composes first song. In Munich, Weber produces his one-act Singspiel *Abu Hassan*.

1812 D., Dussek. B., Flotow, Thalberg. Schubert begins lessons with Salieri. Première of Rossini's opera *La Scala di seta*. Spohr becomes leader of orchestra at the Theater-an-der Wien.

1813 D., Grétry, B., Wagner, Verdi, Dargomijsky, Henry Smart. In Vienna, Friends of Music organized. London Philharmonic founded by Salomon. In Venice, Rossini's first great successes: *Tancredi* and *L'Italiana in Algeri*. Schubert comp. First Sym.

1814 D., Dr. Burney, Abt Vogler, Prince C. Lichnowsky (Beethoven's patron). In Baltimore, F. S. Key writes *The Star-Spangled Banner*, and it is sung in public. Schubert composes many songs, incl. *Gretchen am Spinnrade*. Peters music-publishing firm founded in Leipzig.

1811 B., Greeley, Wendell Phillips, John Bright, Thackeray. Wellington's victory at Albuera, capture of Badajoz and Ciudad Rodrigo. Jane Austen's *Sense and Sensibility* published.

1812 B., Dickens, Browning, H. B. Stowe, Edward Lear. U. S. declares war on Gt. Britain; *Constitution* captures *Guerrière*. Napoleon starts his Russian campaign; Russians retreat, burning Moscow. Pub. of Byron's *Childe Harold*, Grimms' *Fairy Tales*.

1813 B., Livingstone, Bessemer, Frémont, Stephen A. Douglas. Madison's 2d inaug. Perry's victory on Lake Erie. Vigorous campaign of European allies against French; battles of Dresden, Lützen, Leipzig, Vitoria. Southey made Poet Laureate. Austen's *Pride and Prejudice*, pub.

1814 B., Charles Reade, Motley, Lermontov, Stanton, Philip Kearny. Allied armies advance on Paris; Napoleon exiled to Elba; Louis XVIII signs first Peace of Paris; Congress of Vienna opens to fix terms. British burn Washington bldgs.; war ends; peace signed at Ghent. Stephenson invents locomotive.

1815 On death of his brother Carl, takes charge of nephew; long and troublesome litigation opens over custody. Quarrel with Stephan von Breuning, and estrangement. Composes very few works.

1816 Litigation over nephew's custody continues. Comp. song cycle *An die ferne Geliebte*. Vienna confers on him the freedom of the city. Publ. *Archduke* Trio and other works.

1817 Receives a piano from Broadwood in London. Begins Ninth (Choral) Symphony. Health prevents his accepting invitation to go to England.

1818 Begins comp. of *Missa Solemnis* and writes *Hammerklavier* Sonata. Summer and autumn at Mödling; health improves.

1815 D., Salomon. B., Kjerulf, Robert Franz. Schubert comp. *Erlkönig* and many other songs (eight on Oct. 13 alone). In Boston, Handel and Haydn Society org. Spohr makes concert tour, plays with Paganini in Rome.

1816 D., Prince Lobkowitz, Beethoven's patron and friend. In Rome, première of Rossini's *The Barber of Seville*. Schubert's songs incl. *The Wanderer*. Mälzel constructs first metronome.

1817 D., Méhul, Monsigny. Schubert leaves Lichtenthal school, lives in Vienna. Rossini produces *La Cenerentola*. In Dresden, Weber reorganizes the Royal Opera.

1818 B., Gounod, Litolff, Kullak. Handel and Haydn Society in Boston gives the first American performance of Handel's *Messiah*.

1815 B., Bismarck, Trollope, R. H. Dana. In January, Gen. Jackson (not knowing peace has been signed) wins Battle of New Orleans. Napoleon escapes, goes to Paris, moves with army into Belgium; defeated by allies at Waterloo; sent to final exile on St. Helena.

1816 B., Charlotte Brontë. Humphry Davy invents miner's safety lamp. Shelley marries Mary Godwin. Byron leaves England for good. Congress passes protective tariff. Coleridge's *Kubla Khan* and *Christabel*; Austen's *Emma*; Scott's *Antiquary*, pub.

1817 D., Mme. de Staël, Kosciusko, J. Austen. B., Thoreau, Mommsen, Fredk. Douglass. Monroe inaug. Ground broken for Erie Canal. First Seminole War in Florida. Keats's *Poems* and Bryant's *Thanatopsis*.

1818 D., Paul Revere, George Rogers Clark, "Light-Horse Harry" Lee, Caspar Wistar. B., Karl Marx, Emily Brontë, Maria Mitchell, Turgenev. U. S. flag in its present form is first raised on the Capitol. Mary Shelley's *Frankenstein*; Austen's *Northanger Abbey* and *Persuasion*; Keats's *Endymion*; Scott's *Rob Roy*, published.

1820 Wins lawsuit and regains custody of nephew.

1821 Comp. and publishes Pf. Sonata in E, Opus 109, and continues to work on Ninth Symphony.

1822 Meets Rossini, who is visiting Vienna. Goes on with *Missa Solemnis* and Ninth Symphony. Composes *Consecration of the House* Overture.

1823 Publishes *Diabelli* Variations and finishes Ninth Symphony and *Missa*.

1824 Begins comp. of "last quartets," writing Opus 127. World première of *Missa Solemnis* and Symphony No. 9 (*Choral*) on May 7 in Vienna.

1820 B., Jenny Lind. Fr. Liszt (aged 9) makes first public appearance. C. M. von Weber's *Freischütz* Overture is performed.

1821 Weber's *Freischütz* (complete opera) is prod. in Berlin. Schubert's *Erlkönig* first sung in public. American prem. of Beethoven's First Symphony is given in Philadelphia.

1822 B., César Franck. Schubert calls on Beethoven; completes *Alfonso and Estrella*; stops work on B minor (Unfinished) Symphony.

1823 D., Waldstein, Beethoven's patron. Premières of Weber's *Euryanthe*, Rossini's *Semiramide*, Schubert's *Rosamunde. Home, Sweet Home* is first sung (in opera *Clari*), London.

1824 D., Viotti. B., Smetana, Bruckner. Liszt (aged 13) gives London concerts. Schubert composes Quartet in A minor, Octet in F, Grand Duo, and other works.

1820 D., Danl. Boone, George III. B., Anne Brontë, F. Nightingale. Missouri Compromise passed. Irving's *Sketch Book* and Keats's *Lamia* published.

1821 D., Keats, Bonaparte. B., Helmholtz, Flaubert, Dostoevski. Monroe's 2d inauguration. War of Greek Independence begins. Cooper's *Spy*, Scott's *Kenilworth*, Shelley's *Adonais*, published.

1822 D., Shelley. B., Pasteur, Mendel, Rosa Bonheur, U. S. Grant. Brazil becomes empire. Ecuador wins independence. Rosetta Stone deciphered by Champollion. Lamb's *Essays of Elia* (first series) published. Austin founds 1st American settlement in Texas.

1823 B., Renan, Fabre, Parkman, Monroe, in message to Congress, proclaims what will later be called the Monroe Doctrine. Mexico becomes a republic. Scott's *Quentin Durward* pub.

1824 D., Byron. B., Stonewall Jackson, Dumas *fils*, Wilkie Collins. Lafayette visits U. S. Jim Bridger is first white man to see Great Salt Lake. U. S. Bureau of Indian Affairs is organized. Lafayette visits U. S.

1825 Composes Quartets in B-flat and A minor (Opp. 130, 132).

1825 D., Salieri. B., Johann Strauss, Jr. Munich Opera House is opened. First serious comp. of Franz Liszt, operetta *Don Sancho*, produced in Paris. Première of Boieldieu's opera *La Dame blanche*.

1825 D., Eli Whitney, "Jean Paul" Richter. B., Huxley, Bayard Taylor. Inaug. of John Quincy Adams. Erie Canal opened. Robert Owen founds colony in New Harmony, Ind. "Decembrist" uprising in Russia. First ed. of Pepys's *Diary* published.

1826 With writing of Quartets in C-sharp minor and F (Opp. 131, 135), the "last quartets" are finished. Nephew attempts suicide, and—in taking him to Gneixendorf—Beethoven catches cold and develops ailments leading to final illness.

1826 D., Carl Maria von Weber. B., Stephen C. Foster. Premières of Mendelssohn's *Midsummer Night's Dream* Overture, Weber's *Oberon*, Spohr's *Last Judgment*, Schubert's *Death and the Maiden* Quartet.

1826 D., John Adams, Thomas Jefferson, the pirate Jean Lafitte. B., the elder Sothern, Empress Eugénie. Pub. of Burke's *Peerage* (1st ed.), Cooper's *Last of the Mohicans*.

1827 Dies on March 26, and is buried on March 29 in Währing Cemetery after a public funeral.

1827 At Beethoven's funeral, Schubert is a torch-bearer. He comp. B-flat Trio, *Moments musicaux*, etc., and completes *Winterreise* song-cycle.

1827 D., Blake, Böcklin, Volta, Canning, Laplace. B., Lister, Holman Hunt, Lew Wallace, Gen. McClellan. The English-French-Russian fleets defeat Turkish at Navarino. Pub. of Tennyson's first poems, Poe's *Tamerlane*, De Quincey's *On Murder*.

INDEX